THE POETRY COLLECTION

The
POETRY
Collection

Chosen by Neil Philip
Illustrated by Kate Aldous

WH SMITH
EXCLUSIVE
· BOOKS ·

For my mother with love

NP

For my mother with love

KA

First published 1992
An Albion Book

Produced exclusively for W H Smith Ltd
1992

Conceived, designed and produced by
The Albion Press Ltd, P.O. Box 52, Princes Risborough,
Aylesbury, Bucks HP17 9PR

Designer: Emma Bradford
Copy editor: Elizabeth Wilkes
Permissions: Nick Wetton

ISBN 1 871927 01 3

Typesetting and colour origination by York House, London
Printed and bound in Great Britain by Bath Press Colourbooks

Contents

Early Days

The World Around Us

Tell Me a Tale

People We Know

Pause for Thought

The Animal Kingdom

Magic and Imagination

Early Days

A Peck of Gold

Dust always blowing about the town,
Except when sea-fog laid it down,
And I was one of the children told
Some of the blowing dust was gold.

All the dust the wind blew high
Appeared like gold in the sunset sky,
But I was one of the children told
Some of the dust was really gold.

Such was life in the Golden Gate:
Gold dusted all we drank and ate,
And I was one of the children told,
"We all must eat our peck of gold."

ROBERT FROST

"Little girl, be careful what you say"

Little girl, be careful what you say
when you make talk with words, words –
for words are made of syllables
and syllables, child, are made of air –
and air is so thin – air is the breath of God –
air is finer than fire or mist,
finer than water or moonlight,
finer than spider-webs in the moon,
finer than water-flowers in the morning:
   and words are strong, too,
   stronger than rocks or steel
stronger than potatoes, corn, fish, cattle,
and soft, too, soft as little pigeon-eggs,
soft as the music of hummingbird wings.
   So little girl, when you speak greetings,
when you tell jokes, make wishes or prayers,
   be careful, be careless, be careful,
   be what you wish to be.

CARL SANDBURG

18

"maggie and milly and molly and may"

maggie and milly and molly and may
went down to the beach (to play one day)

and maggie discovered a shell that sang
so sweetly she couldn't remember her troubles, and

milly befriended a stranded star
whose rays five languid fingers were;

and molly was chased by a horrible thing
which raced sideways while blowing bubbles: and

may came home with a smooth round stone
as small as a world and as large as alone.

For whatever we lose (like a you or a me)
it's always ourselves we find in the sea

E.E. CUMMINGS

a song in the front yard

I've stayed in the front yard all my life.
I want a peek at the back
Where it's rough and untended and hungry weed grows.
A girl gets sick of a rose.

I want to go in the back yard now
And maybe down the alley,
To where the charity children play.
I want a good time today.

They do some wonderful things.
They have some wonderful fun.
My mother sneers, but I say it's fine
How they don't have to go in at quarter to nine.
My mother, she tells me that Johnnie Mae
Will grow up to be a bad woman.
That George'll be taken to Jail soon or late
(On account of last winter he sold our back gate).

But I say it's fine. Honest, I do.
And I'd like to be a bad woman, too,
And wear the brave stockings of night-black lace
And strut down the streets with paint on my face.

GWENDOLYN BROOKS

*"My parents kept me from
children who were rough"*

My parents kept me from children who were rough
Who threw words like stones and who wore torn clothes.
Their thighs showed through rags. They ran in the street
And climbed cliffs and stripped by the country streams.

I feared more than tigers their muscles like iron
Their jerking hands and their knees tight on my arms.
I feared the salt coarse pointing of those boys
Who copied my lisp behind me on the road.

They were lithe, they sprang out behind hedges
Like dogs to bark at my world. They threw mud
While I looked the other way, pretending to smile.
I longed to forgive them, but they never smiled.

STEPHEN SPENDER

Knoxville, Tennessee

I always like summer
best
you can eat fresh corn
from daddy's garden
and okra
and greens
and cabbage
and lots of
barbecue
and buttermilk
and homemade ice-cream

at the church picnic
and listen to
gospel music
outside
at the church
homecoming
and go to the mountains with
your grandmother
and go barefooted
and be warm
all the time
not only when you go to bed
and sleep

NIKKI GIOVANNI

Going Down Hill on a Bicycle

A Boy's Song

With lifted feet, hands still,
I am poised, and down the hill
Dart, with heedful mind;
The air goes by in a wind.

Swifter and yet more swift,
Till the heart with a mighty lift
Makes the lungs laugh, the throat cry:–
"O bird, see; see, bird, I fly.

"Is this, is this your joy?
O bird, then I, though a boy,
For a golden moment share
Your feathery life in air!"

Say, heart, is there aught like this
In a world that is full of bliss?
'Tis more than skating, bound
Steel-shod to the level ground.

Speed slackens now, I float
Awhile in my airy boat;
Till, when the wheels scarce crawl,
My feet to the treadles fall.

Alas, that the longest hill
Must end in a vale; but still,
Who climbs with toil, wheresoe'er,
Shall find wings waiting there.

HENRY CHARLES BEECHING

Coming From Kansas

Whenever they come from Kansas
they stay for nearly a week
and they live with Grandma in Council Bluffs
because her house has room enough,
and we go over the day they arrive.
Everyone shouts when they pull in the drive.
We kiss and hug and I get to play
with my cousin Joan most every day
    and the grown-ups cry when they leave.

Whenever they say they're coming,
we make a lot of plans.
Joan and I like to put on a play
and we start to write it the very first day.
There're costumes and sets and curtains to do;
we write a part for the neighbor boy, too,
Denny, who comes in the very first scene
to introduce Joan, who's always the queen
    and I have to be the king.

And when it's hot in the afternoons
we get a big glass of Kool-Aid
and play cribbage or jacks on the vestibule floor
and Denny, the boy who lives next door,
comes over and dares us to go up the hill
where the cemetery, dark and still,
lies spooky with ghosts. We go before night,
but Denny and Joan always get in a fight
    and I have to take Joan's side.

Whenever they come in summer,
Joan tells me about her friends.
She says that Kansas is better, too,
there's always more fun and things to do.
But when we visited there last year
I saw her friends, and they all were queer,
and I told her so, and her face got tight
and then we had a terrible fight
   and we pulled each other's hair.

When we go to Grandma's in autumn,
Joan isn't there any more,
and Denny comes over. There's so much to do
like racing down North Second Avenue
or daring each other to slide down the eaves
or sloshing the puddles and jumping in leaves
and if we decide to write out a scene
Denny will always let me be queen
   and I don't have to bother with Joan!

MYRA COHN LIVINGSTON

25

Little Orphant Annie

Little Orphant Annie's come to our house to stay,
An' wash the cups an' saucers up, an' brush the crumbs away,
An' shoo the chickens off the porch, an' dust the hearth, an' sweep,
An' make the fire, an' bake the bread, an' earn her board-an'-keep;
An' all us other children, when the supper things is done,
We set around the kitchen fire an' has the mostest fun
A-list'nin' to the witch-tales 'at Annie tells about,
An' the Gobble-uns 'at gits you
      Ef you
          Don't
              Watch
                  Out!

Onc't they was a little boy wouldn't say his prayers, –
So when he went to bed at night, away up stairs,
His Mammy heerd him holler, an' his Daddy heerd him bawl,
An' when they turn't the kivvers down, he wasn't there at all!
An' they seeked him in the rafter-room, an' cubby-hole, an' press,
An' seeked him up the chimbly-flue, an' ever'wheres, I guess;
But all they ever found was thist his pants an' roundabout –
An' the Gobble-uns'll git you
      Ef you
          Don't
              Watch
                  Out!

An' one time a little girl 'ud allus laugh an' grin,
An' make fun of ever'one, an' all her blood an' kin;
An' onc't, when they was "company", an' ole folks was there,
She mocked 'em an' shocked 'em, an' said she didn't care!
An' thist as she kicked her heels, an' turn't to run an' hide,
They was two great big Black Things a-standin' by her side,
An' they snatched her through the ceilin' 'fore she knowed what
   she's about!
An' the Gobble-uns'll git you
       Ef you
           Don't
               Watch
                   Out!

An' little Orphant Annie says when the blaze is blue,
An' the lamp-wick sputters, an' the wind goes *woo-oo!*
An' you hear the crickets quit, an' the moon is gray,
An' the lightnin'-bugs in dew is all squenched away, –
You better mind yer parents, an' yer teachers fond an' dear,
An' churish them 'at loves you, an' dry the orphant's tear,
An' he'p the pore an' needy ones 'at clusters all about,
Er the Gobble-uns'll git you
       Ef you
           Don't
               Watch
                   Out!

JAMES WHITCOMB RILEY

kivvers, covers, i.e. bedclothes
roundabout, short jacket

Matilda

who told lies, and was burned to death

Matilda told such Dreadful Lies,
It made one Gasp and Stretch one's Eyes;
Her Aunt, who from her Earliest Youth,
Had kept a Strict Regard for Truth,
Attempted to Believe Matilda:
The effort very nearly killed her,
And would have done so, had not She
Discovered this Infirmity.
For once, towards the Close of Day,
Matilda, growing tired of play,

And finding she was left alone,
Went tiptoe to the Telephone
And summoned the Immediate Aid
Of London's Noble Fire-Brigade.
Within an hour the Gallant Band
Were pouring in on every hand,
From Putney, Hackney Downs and Bow.
With Courage high and Hearts a-glow,
They galloped, roaring through the Town,
"Matilda's House is Burning Down!"
Inspired by British Cheers and Loud
Proceeding from the Frenzied Crowd,
They ran their ladders through a score
Of windows on the Ball Room Floor;

That Night a Fire DID break out –
You should have heard Matilda Shout!
You should have heard her Scream and Bawl,
And throw the window up and call
To People passing in the Street –
(The rapidly increasing Heat
Encouraging her to obtain
Their confidence) – but all in vain!
For every time She shouted "Fire!"
They only answered "Little Liar!"
And therefore when her Aunt returned,
Matilda, and the House, were Burned.

HILAIRE BELLOC

And took Peculiar Pains to Souse
The Pictures up and down the House,
Until Matilda's Aunt succeeded
In showing them they were not needed;
And even then she had to pay
To get the Men to go away!
It happened that a few Weeks later
Her Aunt was off to the Theatre
To see that Interesting Play
The Second Mrs Tanqueray.
She had refused to take her Niece
To hear that Entertaining Piece:
A Deprivation Just and Wise
To Punish her for Telling Lies.

The Toys

My little Son, who look'd from thoughtful eyes
And moved and spoke in quiet grown-up wise,
Having my law the seventh time disobey'd,
I struck him, and dismiss'd
With hard words and unkiss'd,
– His Mother, who was patient, being dead.
Then, fearing lest his grief should hinder sleep,
I visited his bed,
But found him slumbering deep,
With darken'd eyelids, and their lashes yet
From his late sobbing wet.
And I, with moan,
Kissing away his tears, left others of my own;
For, on a table drawn beside his head,
He had put, within his reach,
A box of counters and a red-vein'd stone,
A piece of glass abraded by the beach.

And six or seven shells,
A bottle with bluebells,
And two French copper coins, ranged there with careful art,
To comfort his sad heart.
So when that night I pray'd
To God, I wept, and said:
Ah, when at last we lie with trancèd breath,
Not vexing Thee in death,
And Thou rememberest of what toys
We made our joys,
How weakly understood
Thy great commanded good,
Then, fatherly not less
Than I whom Thou has moulded from the clay,
Thou'lt leave Thy wrath, and say,
"I will be sorry for their childishness."

COVENTRY PATMORE

Childhood

I used to think that grown-up people chose
To have stiff backs and wrinkles round their nose,
And veins like small fat snakes on either hand,
On purpose to be grand.
Till through the banisters I watched one day
My great-aunt Etty's friend who was going away,
And how her onyx beads had come unstrung.
I saw her grope to find them as they rolled;
And then I knew that she was helplessly old,
And I was helplessly young.

FRANCES CORNFORD

Oliver Twist

Oliver Twist can't do this
if so do so
touch your toe under we go
touch the ground and a merry go round,
and mother oh lady says to jump
mother oh grady says to cry
mother oh lady says be white
mother oh grady says be black,
     brown black
     yellow black
     black black
     black pickney stamped English
singing brown skin girl
stay home and mind baby,
growing up la di dah polite
pleasing and thank you ma'm, yet so savage
     union jacked in red
     in white
     in blue
and dyed in black to welcome Her
tiny hand moving slowly backward
slowly forward
painted smile on regal face
from the stately "buh look how shiny"
black limousine with air conditioned crawl,
and little children faint and drop
black flies in the heat singing
Britons never never never
shall be slaves and
all that land of hope and glory
that was not,

black flies in the heat singing
of Hector and Lysander
and such great names as these,
but of all the world's great heroes
there's none that can compare
with a tow row row row row row
of the British Grenadiers and
little black children
marching past stiffly white bloused
skirted blue
overalled and goin' to one big school
feelin' we self look so proper –
a cut above our parents you know,
man we was black
an' we was proud
we had we independence
an' massa day done,
we goin' to wear dat uniform
perch dat hat
'pon we hot comb head
jus' like all dem school girls
roun' de empire
learning about odes to nightingales
forget hummingbirds,
a king that forgot
Harriet Tubman, Sojourner Truth
and burnt his cakes,
about princes shut in towers
not smelly holds of stinking ships
and pied piper to our blackest dreams
a bastard mother, from her weaned
on silent names of stranger lands.

MARLENE PHILIP

33

The School Children

The children go forward with their little satchels.
And all morning the mothers have labored
to gather the late apples, red and gold,
like words of another language.

And on the other shore
are those who wait behind great desks
to receive these offerings.

How orderly they are – the nails
on which the children hang
their overcoats of blue or yellow wool.

And the teachers shall instruct them in silence
and the mothers shall scour the orchards for a way out,
drawing to themselves the gray limbs of the fruit trees
bearing so little ammunition.

LOUISE GLÜCK

Wagtail and Baby

A baby watched a ford, whereto
    A wagtail came for drinking;
A blaring bull went wading through,
    The wagtail showed no shrinking.

A stallion splashed his way across,
    The birdie nearly sinking;
He gave his plumes a twitch and toss,
    And held his own unblinking.

Next saw the baby round the spot
    A mongrel slowly slinking;
The wagtail gazed, but faltered not
    In dip and sip and prinking.

A perfect gentleman then neared;
    The wagtail, in a winking,
With terror rose and disappeared;
    The baby fell a-thinking.

THOMAS HARDY

35

Incident

Once riding in old Baltimore,
    Heart-filled, head-filled with glee,
I saw a Baltimorean
    Keep looking straight at me.

Now I was eight and very small,
    And he was no whit bigger,
And so I smiled, but he poked out
    His tongue, and called me, "Nigger."

I saw the whole of Baltimore
    From May until December;
Of all the things that happened there
    That's all that I remember.

COUNTEE CULLEN

36

Black Girl in the Rain

Hey little girl
with your
high crowned
natural head
thrown back to laugh
as the rain runs down your face.

Cares forgot
Hair forgot
Drawn up in
tight little curls
that grace your sunbaked brow.

Spin,
    Dance,
        Enjoy the rain's warm fingers,
            tickling, teasing ecstasy.

LORRAINE F. JOSEPH

It Was Long Ago

I'll tell you, shall I, something I remember?
Something that still means a great deal to me.
It was long ago.

A dusty road in summer I remember,
A mountain, and an old house, and a tree
That stood, you know,

Behind the house. An old woman I remember
In a red shawl with a grey cat on her knee
Humming under a tree.

She seemed the oldest thing I can remember,
But then perhaps I was not more than three.
It was long ago.

EARLY DAYS

I dragged on the dusty road, and I remember
How the old woman looked over the fence at me
And seemed to know

How it felt to be three, and called out, I remember
"Do you like bilberries and cream for tea?"
I went under the tree

And while she hummed, and the cat purred, I remember
How she filled a saucer with berries and cream for me
So long ago,

Such berries and such cream as I remember
I never had seen before, and never see
Today, you know.

And that is almost all I can remember,
The house, the mountain, the grey cat on her knee,
Her red shawl, and the tree,

And the taste of the berries, the feel of the sun I remember,
And the smell of everything that used to be
So long ago,

Till the heat on the road outside again I remember,
And how the long dusty road seemed to have for me
No end, you know.

That is the farthest thing I can remember.
It won't mean much to you. It does to me.
Then I grew up, you see.

ELEANOR FARJEON

Manners

For a Child of 1918

My grandfather said to me
as we sat on the wagon seat,
"Be sure to remember to always
speak to everyone you meet."

We met a stranger on foot.
My grandfather's whip tapped his hat.
"Good day, sir. Good day. A fine day."
And I said it and bowed where I sat.

Then we overtook a boy we knew
with his big pet crow on his shoulder.
"Always offer everyone a ride;
don't forget that when you get older,"

my grandfather said. So Willy
climbed up with us, but the crow
gave a "Caw!" and flew off. I was worried.
How would he know where to go?

But he flew a little way at a time
from fence post to fence post, ahead;
and when Willy whistled he answered.
"A fine bird," my grandfather said,

"and he's well brought up. See, he answers
nicely when he's spoken to.
Man or beast, that's good manners.
Be sure that you both always do."

When automobiles went by,
the dust hid the people's faces,
but we shouted "Good day! Good day!
Fine Day!" at the top of our voices.

When we came to Hustler Hill,
he said that the mare was tired,
so we all got down and walked,
as our good manners required.

ELIZABETH BISHOP

"I Remember, I Remember"

I remember, I remember
The house where I was born,
The little window where the sun
Came peeping in at morn;
He never came a wink too soon
Nor brought too long a day;
But now, I often wish the night
Had borne my breath away.

I remember, I remember
The roses, red and white,
The violets, and the lily-cups –
Those flowers made of light!
The lilacs where the robin built,
And where my brother set
The laburnum on his birthday, –
The tree is living yet!

I remember, I remember
Where I was used to swing,
And thought the air must rush as fresh
To swallows on the wing;
My spirit flew in feathers then
That is so heavy now,
And summer pools could hardly cool
The fever on my brow.

I remember, I remember
The fir trees dark and high;
I used to think their slender tops
Were close against the sky:
It was a childish ignorance,
But now 'tis little joy
To know I'm farther off from Heaven
Than when I was a boy.

THOMAS HOOD

The World Around Us

Cargoes

Quinquireme of Nineveh from distant Ophir
Rowing home to haven in sunny Palestine,
With a cargo of ivory,
And apes and peacocks,
Sandalwood, cedarwood, and sweet white wine.

Stately Spanish galleon coming from the Isthmus,
Dipping through the Tropics by the palm-green shores,
With a cargo of diamonds,
Emeralds, amethysts,
Topazes, and cinnamon, and gold moidores.

Dirty British coaster with a salt-caked smoke stack
Butting through the Channel in the mad March days,
With a cargo of Tyne coal,
Road-rail, pig-lead,
Firewood, iron-ware, and cheap tin trays.

JOHN MASEFIELD

"Upon the hearth the fire is red"

Upon the hearth the fire is red,
Beneath the roof there is a bed;
But not yet weary are our feet,
Still round the corner we may meet
A sudden tree or standing stone
That none have seen but we alone.
   Tree and flower and leaf and grass,
   Let them pass! Let them pass!
   Hill and water under sky,
   Pass them by! Pass them by!

Still round the corner there may wait
A new road or a secret gate,
And though we pass them by today,
Tomorrow we may come this way
And take the hidden paths that run
Towards the Moon or to the Sun.
   Apple, thorn, and nut and sloe,
   Let them go! Let them go!
   Sand and Stone and pool and dell,
   Fare you well! Fare you well!

Home is behind, the world ahead,
And there are many paths to tread
Through shadows to the edge of night,
Until the stars are all alight.
Then world behind and home ahead,
We'll wander back to home and bed.
   Mist and twilight, cloud and shade,
   Away shall fade! Away shall fade!
   Fire and lamp, and meat and bread,
   And then to bed! And then to bed!

J.R.R. TOLKIEN

The World's End

The clouds are high and the skies are wide
  (It's a weary way to the world's end).
I hear the wind upon a hillside
  (Over the hills, away).

Over the hills and over the sea
  (It's a weary way to the world's end).
The woman alone is a-calling me
  (Over the hills, away).

Beyond the rim of the rising moon
  (It's a weary way to the world's end).
He's back too late who starts too soon
  (Over the hills, away).

He's wise, and he laughs who loves to roam
  (It's a weary way to the world's end);
He's wise and he cries the when he comes home
  (Over the hills, away).

Woman alone, and all alone
  (It's a weary way to the world's end).
I'll just be sitting at home, my own,
  The world's a weary way.

HILAIRE BELLOC

The Unexplorer

There was a road ran past our house
Too lovely to explore.
I asked my mother once – she said
That if you followed where it led
It brought you to the milk-man's door.
(That's why I have not travelled more.)

EDNA ST VINCENT MILLAY

A Mill

Two leaps the water from its race
    Made to the brook below;
The first leap it was curving glass,
    The second bounding snow.

WILLIAM ALLINGHAM

Ha'nacker Mill

Sally is gone that was so kindly
    Sally is gone from Ha'nacker Hill.
And the Briar grows ever since then so blindly
    And ever since then the clapper is still,
    And the sweeps have fallen from Ha'nacker Mill.

Ha'nacker Hill is in Desolation:
    Ruin a-top and a field unploughed.
And Spirits that call on a fallen nation
    Spirits that loved her calling aloud:
    Spirits abroad in a windy cloud.

Spirits that call and no one answers;
    Ha'nacker's down and England's done.
Wind and Thistle for pipe and dancers
    And never a ploughman under the Sun.
    Never a ploughman. Never a one.

HILAIRE BELLOC

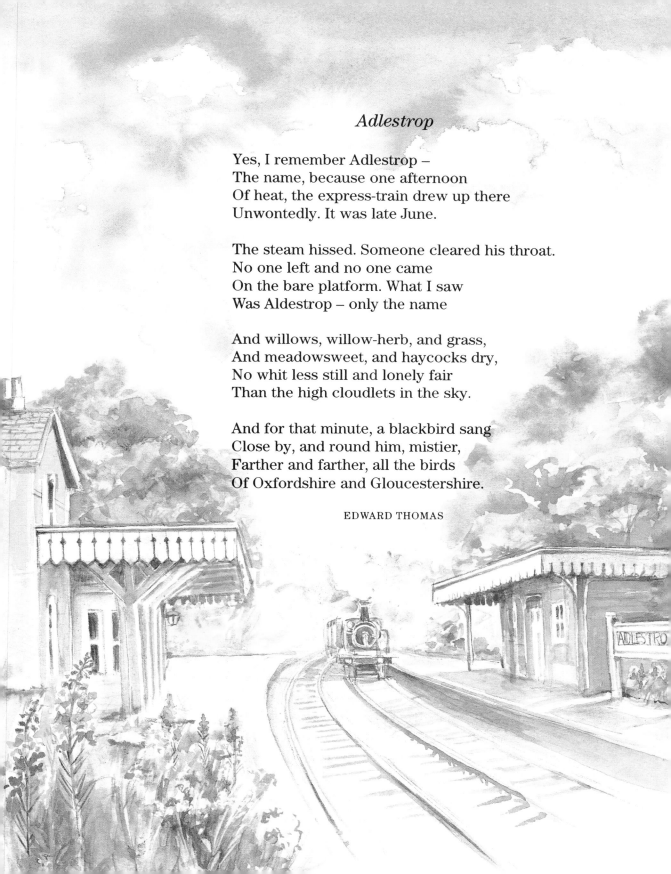

Adlestrop

Yes, I remember Adlestrop –
The name, because one afternoon
Of heat, the express-train drew up there
Unwontedly. It was late June.

The steam hissed. Someone cleared his throat.
No one left and no one came
On the bare platform. What I saw
Was Aldestrop – only the name

And willows, willow-herb, and grass,
And meadowsweet, and haycocks dry,
No whit less still and lonely fair
Than the high cloudlets in the sky.

And for that minute, a blackbird sang
Close by, and round him, mistier,
Farther and farther, all the birds
Of Oxfordshire and Gloucestershire.

EDWARD THOMAS

The Codfish Shanty

Cape Cod girls they've got no combs,
    Heave away, heave away,
They comb their hair with codfish bones,
    And we're bound for South Australia.
      Heave away, my bully-bully boys,
      Heave away, heave away.
      Heave away, why don't you make some noise?
      And we're bound for South Australia.

Cape Cod boys they have no sleds,
    Heave away, heave away,
They slide down hills on codfish heads,
    And we're bound for South Australia.

Cape Cod cats they've got no tails,
    Heave away, heave away,
They blew away in heavy gales,
    And we're bound for South Australia.

TRADITIONAL

Waltzing Matilda

Once a jolly swagman camped by a billabong,
    Under the shade of a coolabah tree;
And he sang as he watched and waited till his billy boiled,
    "You'll come a-waltzing Matilda with me!"

"Waltzing Matilda, Waltzing Matilda,
    You'll come a-waltzing Matilda with me,"
And he sang as he watched and waited till his billy boiled,
    "You'll come a-waltzing Matilda with me."

Down came a jumbuck to drink at the billabong,
   Up jumped the swagman and grabbed him with glee;
And he sang as he shoved that jumbuck in his tucker-bag,
   "You'll come a-waltzing Matilda with me!"

   "Waltzing Matilda, Waltzing Matilda,
      You'll come a-waltzing Matilda with me,"
   And he sang as he shoved that jumbuck in his tucker-bag,
      "You'll come a-waltzing Matilda with me."

Up rode the squatter mounted on his thoroughbred;
   Down came the troopers – one, two and three.
"Whose the jolly jumbuck you've got in your tucker-bag?
   You'll come a-waltzing Matilda with me."

   "Waltzing Matilda, Waltzing Matilda,
      You'll come a-waltzing Matilda with me.
   Whose the jolly jumbuck you've got in your tucker-bag?
      You'll come a-waltzing Matilda with me."

Up jumped the swagman, sprang into the billabong,
   "You'll never catch me alive," said he.
And his ghost may be heard as you pass by that billabong
   "Who'll come a-waltzing Matilda with me?"

   "Waltzing Matilda, Waltzing Matilda,
      You'll come a-waltzing Matilda with me,"
   And his ghost may be heard as you pass by that billabong,
      "Who'll come a-waltzing Matilda with me?"

BANJO PATERSON

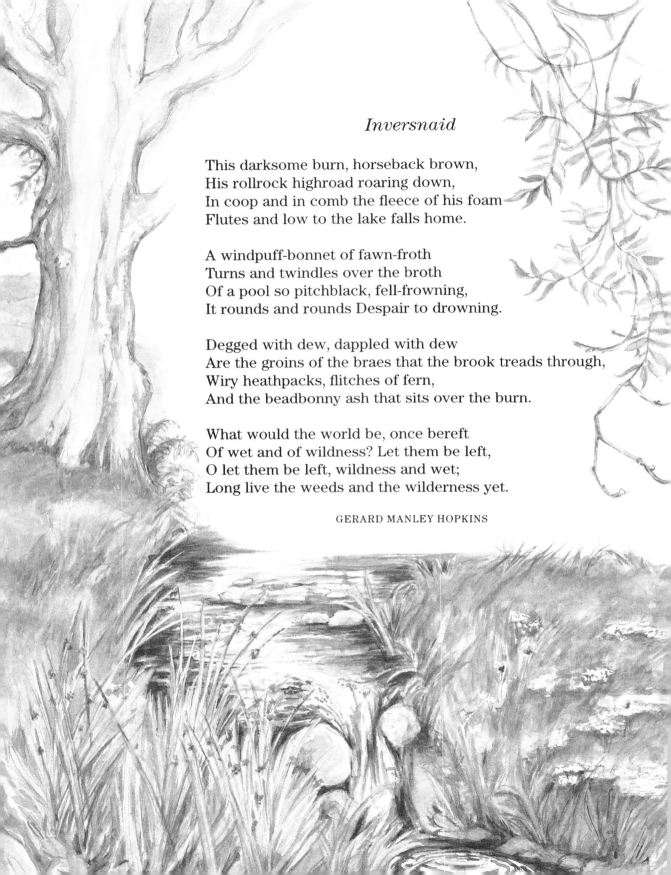

Inversnaid

This darksome burn, horseback brown,
His rollrock highroad roaring down,
In coop and in comb the fleece of his foam
Flutes and low to the lake falls home.

A windpuff-bonnet of fawn-froth
Turns and twindles over the broth
Of a pool so pitchblack, fell-frowning,
It rounds and rounds Despair to drowning.

Degged with dew, dappled with dew
Are the groins of the braes that the brook treads through,
Wiry heathpacks, flitches of fern,
And the beadbonny ash that sits over the burn.

What would the world be, once bereft
Of wet and of wildness? Let them be left,
O let them be left, wildness and wet;
Long live the weeds and the wilderness yet.

GERARD MANLEY HOPKINS

Home Thoughts from Abroad

Oh, to be in England
Now that April's there,
And whoever wakes in England
Sees, some morning, unaware,
That the lowest boughs and the brushwood sheaf
Round the elm-tree bole are in tiny leaf,
While the chaffinch sings on the orchard bough
In England – now!
And after April, when May follows,
And the whitethroat builds, and all the swallows!
Hark, where my blossomed pear-tree in the hedge
Leans to the field and scatters on the clover
Blossoms and dewdrops – at the bent spray's edge –
That's the wise thrush; he sings each song twice over,
Lest you should think he never could recapture
The first fine careless rapture!
And though the fields look rough with hoary dew
All will be gay when noontide wakes anew
The buttercups, the little children's dower
– Far brighter than this gaudy melon-flower!

ROBERT BROWNING

"Flower in the Crannied Wall"

Flower in the crannied wall,
I pluck you out of the crannies,
I hold you here, root and all, in my hand,
Little flower—but *if* I could understand
What you are, root and all, and all in all,
I should know what God and man is.

ALFRED, LORD TENNYSON

51

Landscapes

I. New Hampshire

Children's voices in the orchard
Between the blossom- and the fruit-time:
Golden head, crimson head,
Between the green tip and the root.
Black wing, brown wing, hover over;
Twenty years and the spring is over;
To-day grieves, to-morrow grieves,
Cover me over, light-in-leaves;
Golden head, black wing,
Cling, swing,
Spring, sing,
Swing up into the apple-tree.

II. Virginia

Red river, red river,
Slow flow heat is silence
No will is still as a river
Still. Will heat move
Only through the mocking-bird
Heard once? Still hills
Wait. Gates wait. Purple trees,
White trees, wait, wait,
Delay, decay. Living, living,
Never moving. Ever moving
Iron thoughts came with me
And go with me:
Red river, river, river.

T.S. ELIOT

The Negro Speaks of Rivers

I've known rivers:
I've known rivers ancient as the world and older than the
　　flow of human blood in human veins.

My soul has grown deep like the rivers.

I bathed in the Euphrates when dawns were young.
I built my hut near the Congo and it lulled me to sleep.
I looked upon the Nile and raised the pyramids above it.
I heard the singing of the Mississippi when Abe Lincoln
　　went down to New Orleans, and I've seen its muddy
　　bosom turn all golden in the sunset.

I've known rivers:
Ancient, dusky rivers.

My soul has grown deep like the rivers.

LANGSTON HUGHES

Water Picture

In the pond in the park
all things are doubled:
Long buildings hang and
wriggle gently. Chimneys
are bent legs bouncing
on clouds below. A flag
wags like a fishhook
down there in the sky.

The arched stone bridge
is an eye, with underlid
in the water. In its lens
dip crinkled heads with hats
that don't fall off. Dogs go by,
barking on their backs.
A baby, taken to feed the
ducks, dangles upside-down,
a pink balloon for a buoy.

Treetops deploy a haze of
cherry bloom for roots,
where birds coast belly-up
in the glass bowl of a hill;
from its bottom a bunch
of peanut-munching children
is suspended by their
sneakers, waveringly.

A swan, with twin necks
forming the figure three,
steers between two dimpled
towers doubled. Fondly,
hissing, she kisses herself,
and all the scene is troubled:
water-windows splinter,
tree-limbs tangle, the bridge
folds like a fan.

MAY SWENSON

The River Is a Piece Of Sky

From the top of a bridge
The river below
Is a piece of sky–
   Until you throw
   A penny in
   Or a cockleshell
   Or a pebble or two
   Or a bicycle bell
   Or a cobblestone
   Or a fat man's cane–
And then you can see
It's a river again.

The difference you'll see
When you drop your penny:
The river has splashes,
The sky hasn't any.

JOHN CIARDI

Prelude

Still south I went and west and south again,
Through Wicklow from the morning till the night,
And far from cities, and the sites of men,
Lived with the sunshine and the moon's delight.

I knew the stars, the flowers, and the birds,
The grey and wintry sides of many glens,
And did but half remember human words,
In converse with the mountains, moors, and fens.

J.M. SYNGE

Composed upon Westminster Bridge
Sept. 3, 1802

Earth has not anything to show more fair:
Dull would he be of soul who could pass by
A sight so touching in its majesty:
This City now doth, like a garment, wear
The beauty of the morning; silent, bare,
Ships, towers, domes, theatres, and temples lie
Open unto the fields, and to the sky;
All bright and glittering in the smokeless air.
Never did sun more beautifully steep
In his first splendour, valley, rock, or hill;
Ne'er saw I, never felt, a calm so deep!
The river glideth at his own sweet will:
Dear God! the very houses seem asleep;
And all that mighty heart is lying still!

WILLIAM WORDSWORTH

Symphony in Yellow

An omnibus across the bridge
    Crawls like a yellow butterfly,
    And, here and there, a passer-by
Shows like a little restless midge.

Big barges full of yellow hay
    Are moored against the shadowy wharf,
    And, like a yellow silken scarf,
The thick fog hangs along the quay.

The yellow leaves begin to fade
    And flutter from the Temple elms,
    And at my feet the pale green Thames
Lies like a rod of rippled jade.

OSCAR WILDE

Image

Old houses were scaffolding once
    and workmen whistling.

T.E. HULME

A Windy Day

This wind brings all dead things to life,
Branches that lash the air like whips
And dead leaves rolling in a hurry
Or peering in a rabbit's bury
Or trying to push down a tree;
Gates that fly open to the wind
And close again behind,
And fields that are a flowing sea
And make the cattle look like ships;
Straws glistening and stiff
Lying on air as on a shelf
And pond that leaps to leave itself;
And feathers too that rise and float,
Each feather changed into a bird,
And line-hung sheets that crack and strain;
Even the sun-greened coat,
That through so many winds has served,
The scarecrow struggles to put on again.

ANDREW YOUNG

Tell Me a Tale

For Want of a Nail

For want of a nail, the shoe was lost;
For want of the shoe, the horse was lost;
For want of the horse, the rider was lost;
For want of the rider, the battle was lost;
For want of the battle, the kingdom was lost;
And all from the want of a horseshoe nail.

ANONYMOUS

The Great Day

Hurrah for revolution and more cannon-shot!
A beggar upon horseback lashes a beggar on foot.
Hurrah for revolution and cannon come again!
The beggars have changed places, but the lash goes on.

W.B. YEATS

O Captain! My Captain!

O Captain! my Captain! our fearful trip is done,
The ship has weather'd every rack, the prize we sought is won,
The port is near, the bells I hear, the people all exulting,
While follow eyes the steady keel, the vessel grim and daring;
      But O heart! heart! heart!
        O the bleeding drops of red!
          Where on the deck my Captain lies,
            Fallen cold and dead.

O Captain! my Captain! rise up and hear the bells;
Rise up – for you the flag is flung – for you the bugle trills,
For you bouquets and ribbon'd wreaths – for you the shores
    crowding,
For you they call, the swaying mass, their eager faces turning;
      Here, Captain! dear father!
        This arm beneath your head!
          It is some dream that on the deck
            You've fallen cold and dead.

My Captain does not answer, his lips are pale and still,
My father does not feel my arm, he has no pulse nor will;
The ship is anchor'd safe and sound, its voyage closed and done,
From fearful trip the victor ship comes in with object won;
      Exult, O shores! and ring, O bells!
      But I, with mournful tread,
          Walk the deck my Captain lies,
            Fallen cold and dead.

WALT WHITMAN

Drake's Drum

Drake he's in his hammock an' a thousand mile away,
  (Capten, art tha sleepin' there below?),
Slung atween the round shot in Nombre Dios Bay,
  An' dreamin' arl the time o' Plymouth Hoe.
Yarnder lumes the Island, yarnder lie the ships,
  Wi' sailor lads a dancin' heel-an'-toe,
An' the shore-lights flashin', an' the night-tide dashin',
  He sees et arl so plainly as he saw et long ago.

Drake he was a Devon man, an' rüled the Devon seas,
  (Capten, art tha sleepin' there below?),
Rovin' tho' his death fell, he went wi' heart at ease,
  An' dreamin' arl the time o' Plymouth Hoe.
"Take my drum to England, hang et by the shore,
  Strike et when your powder's runnin' low;
If the Dons sight Devon, I'll quit the port o' Heaven,
  An' drum them up the Channel as we drummed them
    long ago."

Drake he's in his hammock till the great Armadas come,
  (Capten, art tha sleepin' there below?),
Slung atween the round shot, listenin' for the drum,
  An' dreamin' arl the time o' Plymouth Hoe.
Call him on the deep sea, call him up the Sound,
  Call him when ye sail to meet the foe;
Where the old trades' plyin' an' the old flag flyin'
  They shall find him ware an' wakin', as they found him long
    ago!

SIR HENRY NEWBOLT

Stackolee

Now what you all know about this?
An' what you all know about that?
They say Stack killed ole Billy Lyons
'Bout a dammed ole Stetson hat!
Oh, poor, poor, Stackolee!

It was on a dark
And cold stormy night
That Billy Lyons and Stackolee
They had that awful fight.
That bad, that bad man Stackolee!

"Oh, Stackolee, oh, Stackolee,
Please spare my life!
For I have got two babies,
And a darling little wife!"
That bad, that bad man Stackolee!

"I care not for your babies
Nor your darling little wife.
You done ruint my Stetson hat
An' I'm bound to have your life!"
That bad, that bad man Stackolee!

It was no Stetson hat.
He didn't have a good excuse.
They say he killed ole Billy Lyons
'Cause he gave his gal abuse.
Oh poor, poor Stackolee!

Stacko's wench was a good girl,
She was true as steel;
She said "I'll stand by you, Stack,
On you I'm never goin' to squeal!"
Down at the trial of Stackolee.

The judge put on the black cap
His voice was stern and cold
"I sentences you to be hanged
The Lord have mercy on your soul!"
That bad, that bad man Stackolee!

He had a rubber-tired hearse . . .
A lot of rubber-tired hacks
Took ole Stackolee to the cemetery
Never to bring him back
Oh poor, poor Stackolee!

TRADITIONAL

Aunt Sue's Stories

Aunt Sue has a head full of stories.
Aunt Sue has a whole heart full of stories.
Summer nights on the front porch
Aunt Sue cuddles a brown-faced child to her bosom
And tells him stories.

Black slaves
Working in the hot sun,
And black slaves
Walking in the dewy night,
And black slaves
Singing sorrow songs on the banks of a mighty river
Mingle themselves softly
In the flow of old Aunt Sue's voice,
Mingle themselves softly
In the dark shadows that cross and recross
Aunt Sue's stories.

And the dark-faced child, listening,
Knows that Aunt Sue's stories are real stories.
He knows that Aunt Sue never got her stories
Out of any book at all,
But that they came
Right out of her own life.

The dark-faced child is quiet
Of a summer night
Listening to Aunt Sue's stories.

LANGSTON HUGHES

63

Black Jack David

Black Jack David come ridin' through the woods
Singin' so loud and merry
That the green hills all around him ring,
And he charmed the heart of a lady.

"How old are you, my pretty little miss,
How old are you, my lady?"
She answered him with a "Tee, hee, hee,
I'll be sixteen next summer."

"Come, go with me, my pretty little miss,
Come, go with me, my lady;
I'll take you across the deep blue sea
Where you never shall want for money.

"Won't you pull off those high heeled shoes
All made of Spanish leather;
Won't you put on some low heeled shoes?
And we'll ride off together."

She soon pulled off those high heeled shoes
All made of Spanish leather;
She put on those low heeled shoes
And they rode off together.

'Twas late at night when the land-lord come
Inquirin' for his lady.
He was posted by a fair young maid:
"She's gone with Black Jack David."

"Go saddle me my noble steed,
Go bridle me my derby;
I'll ride to the east, I'll ride to the west,
Or overtake my lady."

He rode till he came to the deep below;
The stream was deep and muddy.
Tears came tricklin' down his cheeks,
For there he spied his lady.

"How can you leave your house and land,
How can you leave your baby,
How can you leave your husband dear
To go with Black Jack David?"

"Very well can I leave my house and land,
Very well can I leave my baby,
Much better can I leave my husband dear
To go with Black Jack David.

"I won't come back to you, my love,
Nor I won't come back, my husband;
I wouldn't give a kiss from David's lips
For all your land and money.

"Last night I lay on a feather bed
Beside my husband and baby;
Tonight I lay on the cold damp ground
Beside the Black Jack David."

She soon run through her gay clothing,
Her velvet shoes and stockings;
Her gold ring off her finger was gone,
And the gold plate off her bosom.

"Oh, once I had a house and land,
A feather bed and money,
But now I've come to an old straw pad,
With nothing but Black Jack David."

TRADITIONAL

65

The Charge of the Light Brigade

Half a league, half a league,
Half a league onward,
All in the valley of Death
   Rode the six hundred.
   "Forward, the Light Brigade!
Charge for the guns!" he said.
Into the valley of Death
   Rode the six hundred.

"Forward, the Light Brigade!"
Was there a man dismayed?
Not though the soldier knew
   Some one had blundered.
Theirs not to make reply,
Theirs not to reason why,
Theirs but to do and die.
Into the valley of Death
   Rode the six hundred.

Cannon to right of them,
Cannon to left of them,
Cannon in front of them
   Volleyed and thundered;
Stormed at with shot and shell,
Boldly they rode and well,
Into the jaws of Death,
Into the mouth of Hell
   Rode the six hundred.

Flashed all the sabres bare,
Flashed as they turned in air
Sabring the gunners there,
Charging an army, while
   All the world wondered:
Plunged in the battery-smoke
Right through the line they broke;
Cossack and Russian
Reeled from the sabre-stroke
   Shattered and sundered.
Then they rode back, but not,
   Not the six hundred.

Cannon to right of them,
Cannon to left of them,
Cannon behind them,
   Volleyed and thundered;
Stormed at with shot and shell,
While horse and hero fell,
They that had fought so well
Came through the jaws of Death,
Back from the mouth of Hell,
All that was left of them,
   Left of six hundred.

When can their glory fade?
O the wild charge they made!
  All the world wondered.
Honour the charge they made!
Honour the Light Brigade,
  Noble six hundred!

ALFRED, LORD TENNYSON

Widdecombe Fair

"Tom Pearse, Tom Pearse, lend me your gray mare,"
   All along, down along, out along, lee.
"For I want for to go to Widdecombe Fair,
   Wi' Bill Brewer, Jan Stewer, Peter Gurney, Peter Davy,
     Dan'l Whiddon, Harry Hawk,
   Old Uncle Tom Cobley and all."
     Old Uncle Tom Cobley and all.

"And when shall I see again my gray mare?"
   All along, down along, out along, lee.
"By Friday soon, or Saturday noon,
   Wi' Bill Brewer, Jan Stewer, Peter Gurney, Peter Davy,
     Dan'l Whiddon, Harry Hawk,
   Old Uncle Tom Cobley and all."
     Old Uncle Tom Cobley and all.

Then Friday came and Saturday noon,
   All along, down along, out along, lee.
But Tom Pearse's old mare hath not trotted home,
So Tom Pearse he got up to the top o' the hill,
   All along, down along, out along, lee.
And he seed his old mare down a-making her will,
   Wi' Bill Brewer, Jan Stewer, Peter Gurney, Peter Davy,
     Dan'l Whiddon, Harry Hawk,
   Old Uncle Tom Cobley and all.
     Old Uncle Tom Cobley and all.

So Tom Pearse's old mare her took sick and her died,
   All along, down along, out along, lee.
And Tom he sat down on a stone, and he cried

Wi' Bill Brewer, Jan Stewer, Peter Gurney, Peter Davy,
  Dan'l Whiddon, Harry Hawk,
Old Uncle Tom Cobley and all.
    Old Uncle Tom Cobley and all.

But this isn't the end o' this shocking affair,
  All along, down along, out along, lee.
Nor, though they be dead, of the horrid career
  Of Bill Brewer, Jan Stewer, Peter Gurney, Peter Davy,
    Dan'l Whiddon, Harry Hawk,
  Old Uncle Tom Cobley and all.
    Old Uncle Tom Cobley and all.

When the wind whistles cold on the moor of a night,
  All along, down along, out along, lee.
Tom Pearse's old mare doth appear, gashly white,
  Wi' Bill Brewer, Jan Stewer, Peter Gurney, Peter Davy,
    Dan'l Whiddon, Harry Hawk,
  Old Uncle Tom Cobley and all.
    Old Uncle Tom Cobley and all.

And all the long night he heard skirling and groans,
  All along, down along, out along, lee.
From Tom Pearse's old mare in her rattling bones,
  And from Bill Brewer, Jan Stewer, Peter Gurney, Peter
    Davy, Dan'l Whiddon, Harry Hawk,
  Old Uncle Tom Cobley and all.
    Old Uncle Tom Cobley and all.

TRADITIONAL

The Jumblies

They went to sea in a Sieve, they did,
    In a Sieve they went to sea;
In spite of all their friends could say,
On a winter's morn, on a stormy day,
    In a Sieve they went to sea!
And when the Sieve turned round and round,
And everyone cried, "You'll all be drowned!"
They called aloud, "Our Sieve ain't big,
But we don't care a button! We don't care a fig!
    In a Sieve we'll go to sea!"
      Far and few, far and few,
        Are the lands where the Jumblies live;
        Their heads are green, and their hands are blue,
        And they went to sea in a Sieve.

They sailed away in a Sieve, they did,
    In a sieve they sailed so fast,
With only a beautiful pea-green veil
Tied with a riband by way of a sail,
    To a small tobacco-pipe mast;
And everyone said, who saw them go,
"O won't they be soon upset, you know!
For the sky is dark, and the voyage is long,
And happen what may, it's extremely wrong
    In a Sieve to sail so fast!"
      Far and few, far and few,
        Are the lands where the Jumblies live;
        Their heads are green, and their hands are blue,
        And they went to sea in a Sieve.

The water it soon came in, it did,
    The water soon came in;
So to keep them dry, they wrapped their feet
In a pinky paper all folded neat,
    And they fastened it down with a pin.

And they passed the night in a crockery-jar,
And each of them said, "How wise we are!
Though the sky be dark, and the voyage be long,
Yet we never can think we were rash or wrong,
    While round in our Sieve we spin!"
        Far and few, far and few,
            Are the lands where the Jumblies live;
            Their heads are green, and their hands are blue,
                And they went to sea in a Sieve.

And all night long they sailed away;
    And when the sun went down,
They whistled and warbled a moony song
To the echoing sound of a coppery gong,
    In the shade of the mountains brown.
"O Timballo! How happy we are,

When we live in a sieve and a crockery-jar,
And all night long in the moonlight pale,
We sail away with a pea-green sail,
   In the shade of the mountains brown!"
     Far and few, far and few,
      Are the lands where the Jumblies live;
     Their heads are green, and their hands are blue,
      And they went to sea in a Sieve.

They sailed to the Western Sea, they did,
   To a land all covered with trees,
And they bought an Owl, and a useful Cart,
And a pound of Rice, and a Cranberry Tart,
   And a hive of silvery Bees.
And they bought a Pig, and some green Jack-daws,
And a lovely Monkey with lollipop paws,
And forty bottles of Ring-Bo-Ree,
   And no end of Stilton Cheese.
     Far and few, far and few,
      Are the lands where the Jumblies live;
     Their heads are green, and their hands are blue,
      And they went to sea in a Sieve.

And in twenty years they all came back,
   In twenty years or more,
And everyone said, "How tall they've grown!
For they've been to the Lakes, and the Torrible Zone,
   And the hills of the Chankly Bore";
And they drank their health, and gave them a feast
Of dumplings made of beautiful yeast;
And everyone said, "If we only live,
We too will go to sea in a Sieve, –
   To the hills of the Chankly Bore!"
     Far and few, far and few,
      Are the lands where the Jumblies live;
     Their heads are green, and their hands are blue,
      And they went to sea in a Sieve.

EDWARD LEAR

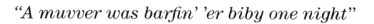

"A muvver was barfin' 'er biby one night"

A muvver was barfin' 'er biby one night,
The youngest of ten and a tiny young mite,
The muvver was poor and the biby was thin,
Only a skelington covered in skin;
The muvver turned rahnd for the soap off the rack,
She was but a moment, but when she turned back,
The biby was gorn; and in anguish she cried,
"Oh, where is my biby?" – The angels replied:

"Your biby 'as fell dahn the plug-'ole,
Your biby 'as gorn dahn the plug;
The poor little thing was so skinny and thin
'E oughter been barfed in a jug;
Your biby is perfeckly 'appy,
'E won't need a barf any more,
Your biby 'as fell dahn the plug-'ole,
Not lorst, but gorn before."

ANONYMOUS

People We Know

"When first my way to fair I took"

When first my way to fair I took
   Few pence in purse had I,
And long I used to stand and look
   At things I could not buy.

Now times are altered: if I care
   To buy a thing, I can;
The pence are here and here's the fair,
   But where's the lost young man?

– To think that two and two are four
   And neither five nor three
The heart of man has long been sore
   And long 'tis like to be.

A.E. HOUSMAN

Up in the Morning Early

Cauld blaws the wind frae east to west,
   The drift is driving sairly;
Sae loud and shrill's I hear the blast –
   I'm sure it's winter fairly.

Up in the morning's no for me,
   Up in the morning early;
When a' the hills are covered wi' snaw,
   I'm sure it's winter fairly.

The birds sit chittering in the thorn,
   A' day they fare but sparely;
And lang's the night frae e'en to morn –
   I'm sure it's winter fairly.

Up in the morning's no for me,
   Up in the morning early;
When a' the hills are covered wi' snaw,
   I'm sure it's winter fairly.

ROBERT BURNS

75

Autobiography

In my childhood trees were green
And there was plenty to be seen.

Come back early or never come.

My father made the walls resound,
He wore his collar the wrong way round.

Come back early or never come.

My mother wore a yellow dress;
Gently, gently, gentleness.

Come back early or never come.

When I was five the black dreams came;
Nothing after was quite the same.

Come back early or never come.

The dark was talking to the dead;
The lamp was dark beside my bed.

Come back early or never come.

When I woke they did not care;
Nobody, nobody was there.

Come back early or never come.

When my silent terror cried,
Nobody, nobody replied.

Come back early or never come.

I got up; the chilly sun
Saw me walk away alone.

Come back early or never come.

LOUIS MACNEICE

To a Poor Old Woman

munching a plum on
the street a paper bag
of them in her hand

They taste good to her
They taste good
to her. They taste
good to her

You can see it by
the way she gives herself
to the one half
sucked out in her hand

Comforted
a solace of ripe plums
seeming to fill the air
They taste good to her

WILLIAM CARLOS WILLIAMS

Poor Kings

God's pity on poor kings,
   They know no gentle rest;
The North and South cry out,
   Cries come from East and West –
"Come, open this new Dock,
   Building, Bazaar, or Fair,"
Lord what a wretched life
   Such men must bear.

They're followed, watched and spied,
   No liberty they know;
Some eye will watch them still,
   No matter where they go.
When in green lanes I muse,
   Alone, and hear birds sing,
God's pity then, say I,
   On some poor king.

W.H. DAVIES

"All the world's a stage"

All the world's a stage,
And all the men and women merely players:
They have their exits and their entrances;
And one man in his time plays many parts,
His acts being seven ages. At first the infant,
Mewling and puking in the nurse's arms.
And then the whining schoolboy, with his satchel,
And shining morning face, creeping like snail
Unwillingly to school. And then the lover,
Sighing like furnace, with a woeful ballad
Made to his mistress' eyebrow. Then a soldier,
Full of strange oaths, and bearded like the pard,
Jealous in honour, sudden and quick in quarrel,
Seeking the bubble reputation
Even in the cannon's mouth. And then the justice,
In fair round belly with good capon lined,
With eyes severe and beard of formal cut,
Full of wise saws and modern instances;
And so he plays his part. The sixth age shifts
Into the lean and slippered pantaloon,
With spectacles on nose, and pouch on side;
His youthful hose, well saved, a world too wide
For his shrunk shank; and his big manly voice,
Turning again toward childish treble, pipes
And whistles in his sound. Last scene of all,
That ends this strange eventful history,
Is second childishness and mere oblivion,
Sans teeth, sans eyes, sans taste, sans everything.

WILLIAM SHAKESPEARE

Meg Merrilies

Old Meg she was a Gipsy,
    And lived upon the Moors:
Her bed it was the brown heath turf,
    And her house was out of doors.

Her apples were swart blackberries,
    Her currants pods o' broom;
Her wine was dew of the wild white rose,
    Her book a churchyard tomb.

Her Brothers were the craggy hills,
    Her Sisters larchen trees –
Alone with her great family
    She lived as she did please.

No breakfast had she many a morn,
    No dinner many a noon,
And 'stead of supper she would stare
    Full hard against the Moon.

But every morn of woodbine fresh
    She made her garlanding,
And every night the dark glen Yew
    She wove, and she would sing.

And with her fingers old and brown
    She plaited Mats of Rushes,
And gave them to the Cottagers
    She met along the Bushes.

Old Meg was brave as Margaret Queen
    And tall as Amazon:
An old red blanket cloak she wore;
    A chip-hat had she on.
God rest her aged bones somewhere –
    She died full long agone!

JOHN KEATS

One

Only one of me
and nobody can get a second one
from a photocopy machine.

Nobody has the fingerprints I have.
Nobody can cry my tears, or laugh my laugh
or have my expectancy when I wait.

But anybody can mimic my dance with my dog.
Anybody can howl how I sing out of tune.
And mirrors can show me multiplied
many times, say, dressed up in red
or dressed up in grey.

Nobody can get into my clothes for me
or feel my fall for me, or do my running.
Nobody hears my music for me, either.

I am just this one.
Nobody else makes the words
I shape with sound, when I talk.

But anybody can act how I stutter in a rage.
Anybody can copy echoes I make.
And mirrors can show me multiplied
many times, say, dressed up in green
or dressed up in blue.

JAMES BERRY

The Fiddler of Dooney

When I play on my fiddle in Dooney,
Folk dance like a wave of the sea;
My cousin is priest in Kilvarnet,
My brother in Mocharabuiee.

I passed my brother and cousin;
They read in their books of prayer;
I read in my book of songs
I bought at the Sligo fair.

When we come at the end of time
To Peter sitting in state,
He will smile on the three old spirits,
But call me first through the gate;

For the good are always the merry,
Save by an evil chance,
And the merry love the fiddle,
And the merry love to dance:

And when the folk there spy me,
They will all come up to me,
With "Here is the fiddler of Dooney!"
And dance like a wave of the sea.

W.B. YEATS

Mocharabuiee, pronounced as if spelt "Mockrabwee"

81

The Solitary Reaper

Behold her, single in the field,
Yon solitary Highland Lass!
Reaping and singing by herself;
Stop here, or gently pass!
Alone she cuts and binds the grain,
And sings a melancholy strain;
O listen! for the Vale profound
Is overflowing with the sound.

No Nightingale did ever chaunt
More welcome notes to weary bands
Of travellers in some shady haunt,
Among Arabian sands:
A voice so thrilling ne'er was heard
In spring-time from the Cuckoo-bird.
Breaking the silence of the seas
Among the farthest Hebrides.

Will no one tell me what she sings?–
Perhaps the plaintive numbers flow
For old, unhappy, far-off things,
And battles long ago:
Or is it some more humble lay,
Familiar matter of to-day?
Some natural sorrow, loss, or pain,
That has been, and may be again?

Whate'er the theme, the Maiden sang
As if her song could have no ending;
I saw her singing at her work,
And o'er the sickle bending;–
I listened, motionless and still;
And, as I mounted up the hill,
The music in my heart I bore,
Long after it was heard no more.

WILLIAM WORDSWORTH

Phizzog

This face you got,
This here phizzog you carry around,
You never picked it out for yourself,
    at all, at all – did you?
This here phizzog – somebody handed it
    to you – am I right?
Somebody said, "Here's yours, now go see
    what you can do with it."
Somebody slipped it to you and it was like
    a package marked:
"No goods exchanged after being taken away" –
This face you got.

CARL SANDBURG

83

My Mother

My mother planted fields
married a man
bore ten children
and still found time
to have her own business
I remember once
she and I
were going to work
the plot of land
she rented from someone
we heard the missionary's car
coming down the road

she jumped over a culvert to hide
because she had on a pair
of my father's pants

the church disapproved of women
wearing men's clothing
when the sun was steadily going westward
we hurried from the field
she had to rush home
to cook the family's meal
she seemed able to do anything
and I think that in one
of her past lives
she was a leader of some sort

my mother planted fields
married a man
bore ten children
and still found time
to run her own business

AFUA COOPER

Lineage

My grandmothers were strong.
They followed plows and bent to toil.
They moved through fields sowing seed.

They touched earth and grain grew.
They were full of sturdiness and singing.
My grandmothers were strong.

My grandmothers are full of memories.
Smelling of soap and onions and wet clay
With veins rolling roughly over quick hands
They have many clean words to say.
My grandmothers were strong.
Why am I not as they?

MARGARET WALKER

The Song of the Old Mother

I rise in the dawn, and I kneel and blow
Till the seed of the fire flicker and glow;
And then I must scrub and bake and sweep
Till stars are beginning to blink and peep;
And the young lie long and dream in their bed
Of the matching of ribbons for bosom and head,
And their day goes over in idleness,
And they sigh if the wind but lift a tress:
While I must work because I am old,
And the seed of the fire gets feeble and cold.

W.B. YEATS

Hay for the Horses

He had driven half the night
From far down San Joaquin
Through Mariposa, up the
Dangerous mountain roads,
And pulled in at eight a.m.
With his big truckload of hay
            behind the barn.
With winch and ropes and hooks
We stacked the bales up clean
To splintery redwood rafters
High in the dark, flecks of alfalfa
Whirling through shingle-cracks of light,
Itch of haydust in the
            sweaty shirt and shoes.
At lunchtime under Black oak
Out in the hot corral,
– The old mare nosing lunchpails,
Grasshoppers crackling in the weeds –
"I'm sixty-eight," he said,
"I first bucked hay when I was seventeen.
I thought, that day I started,
I sure would hate to do this all my life.
And dammit, that's just what
I've gone and done."

GARY SNYDER

An Epilogue

I have seen flowers come in stony places
And kind things done by men with ugly faces,
And the gold cup won by the worst horse at the races,
So I trust, too.

JOHN MASEFIELD

Invictus

Out of the night that covers me,
  Black as the pit from pole to pole,
I thank whatever gods may be
  For my unconquerable soul.

In the fell clutch of circumstance
  I have not winced nor cried aloud.
Under the bludgeonings of chance
  My head is bloody, but unbow'd.

Beyond this place of wrath and tears
  Looms but the Horror of the shade,
And yet the menace of the years
  Finds and shall find me unafraid.

It matters not how strait the gate,
  How charged with punishments the scroll,
I am the master of my fate:
  I am the captain of my soul.

W.E. HENLEY

Life is Fine

I went down to the river,
I set down on the bank.
I tried to think but couldn't,
So I jumped in and sank.

I came up once and hollered!
I came up twice and cried!
If that water hadn't a-been so cold
I might've sunk and died.

    But it was
    Cold in that water!
    It was cold!

I took the elevator
Sixteen floors above the ground.
I thought about my baby
And thought I would jump down.

I stood there and I hollered!
I stood there and I cried!
If it hadn't a-been so high
I might've jumped and died.

    But it was
    High up there!
    It was high!

So since I'm still here livin',
I guess I will live on.
I could've died for love –
But for livin' I was born.

Though you may hear me holler,
And you may see me cry –
I'll be dogged, sweet baby,
If you gonna see me die.

    Life is fine!
    Fine as wine!
    Life is fine!

LANGSTON HUGHES

Mr Jones

"There's been an accident!" they said,
"Your servant's cut in half; he's dead!"
"Indeed!" said Mr Jones, "and please
Send me the half that's got my keys."

HARRY GRAHAM

Pause for Thought

Happy the Man

Happy the man, and happy he alone,
   He who can call today his own:
   He who, secure within, can say,
Tomorrow do thy worst, for I have lived today.
   Be fair or foul or rain or shine
The joys I have possessed, in spite of fate, are mine.
Not Heaven itself upon the past has power,
But what has been, has been, and I have had my hour.

JOHN DRYDEN

"Great things are done"

Great things are done when men and mountains meet;
This is not done by jostling in the street.

WILLIAM BLAKE

If

If you can keep your head when all about you
    Are losing theirs and blaming it on you,
If you can trust yourself when all men doubt you,
    But make allowance for their doubting too;
If you can wait and not be tired by waiting,
    Or being lied about, don't deal in lies,
Or being hated, don't give way to hating,
    And yet don't look too good, nor talk too wise:

If you can dream – and not make dreams your master;
    If you can think – and not make thoughts your aim;
If you can meet with Triumph and Disaster
    And treat those two impostors just the same;
If you can bear to hear the truth you've spoken
    Twisted by knaves to make a trap for fools,
Or watch the things you gave your life to, broken,
    And stoop and build 'em up with worn-out tools:

If you can make one heap of all your winnings
    And risk it on one turn of pitch-and-toss,
And lose, and start again at your beginnings
    And never breathe a word about your loss;
If you can force your heart and nerve and sinew
    To serve your turn long after they are gone,
And so hold on when there is nothing in you
    Except the Will which says to them: "Hold on!"

If you can talk with crowds and keep your virtue,
    Or walk with Kings – nor lose the common touch,
If neither foes nor loving friends can hurt you,
    If all men count with you, but none too much;
If you can fill the unforgiving minute
    With sixty seconds' worth of distance run,
Yours is the Earth and everything that's in it,
    And – which is more – you'll be a Man, my son!

RUDYARD KIPLING

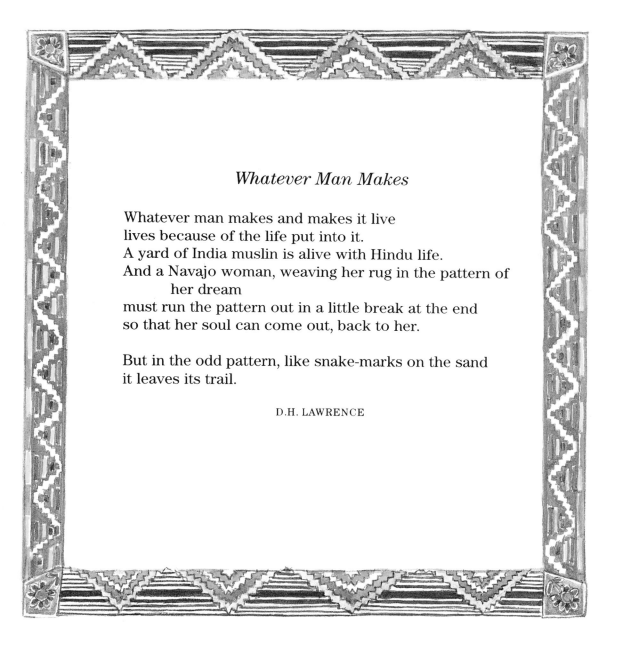

Whatever Man Makes

Whatever man makes and makes it live
lives because of the life put into it.
A yard of India muslin is alive with Hindu life.
And a Navajo woman, weaving her rug in the pattern of
      her dream
must run the pattern out in a little break at the end
so that her soul can come out, back to her.

But in the odd pattern, like snake-marks on the sand
it leaves its trail.

D.H. LAWRENCE

De Ole Sheep Dey Know De Road

Oh, de ole sheep, dey know de road,
De ole sheep, dey know de road,
De ole sheep, dey know de road,
De young lambs must find de way.

My brother, better mind how you walk on de cross,
    De young lambs must find de way,
For your foot might slip, and yo' soul git lost,
    De young lambs must find de way.

Better mind dat sun, and see how she run,
    De young lambs must find de way,
And mind, don't let her catch you wid yo' work undone,
    De young lambs must find de way.

Oh, de ole sheep, dey know de road,
De ole sheep, dey know de road,
De ole sheep, dey know de road,
Young lambs must find de way.

TRADITIONAL

The Donkey

When fishes flew and forests walked,
    And figs grew upon thorn,
Some moment when the moon was blood
    Then surely I was born;

With monstrous head and sickening cry
    And ears like errant wings,
The devil's walking parody
    On all four-footed things.

The tattered outlaw of the earth,
    Of ancient crooked will;
Starve, scourge, deride me: I am dumb,
    I keep my secret still.

Fools! For I also had my hour;
    One far fierce hour and sweet:
There was a shout about my ears,
    And palms before my feet.

G.K. CHESTERTON

93

Ballad of the Bread Man

itchen
bread.
through the window.
r you," he said.

g gold heaven,
his big blue chair,
a mother for his little son.
denly saw you there."

Mary shook and trembled,
  "It isn't true what you say."
"Don't say that," said the angel.
  "The baby's on its way."

Joseph was in the workshop
  Planing a piece of wood.
"The old man's past it," the neighbours
                          said.
  "That girl's been up to no good."

"And who was that elegant fellow,"
  They said, "in the shiny gear?"
The things they said about Gabriel
  Were hardly fit to hear.

Mary never answered,
  Mary never replied.
She kept the information,
  Like the baby, safe inside.

It was election winter.
  They went to vote in town.
When Mary found her time had come
  The hotels let her down.

The baby was born in an annexe
  Next to the local pub.
At midnight, a delegation
  Turned up from the Farmers' Club.

They talked about an explosion
  That made a hole in the sky,
Said they'd been sent to the Lamb & Flag
  To see God come down from on high.

A few days later a bishop
  And a five-star general were seen
With the head of an African country
  In a bullet-proof limousine.

"We've come," they said, "with tokens
  For the little boy to choose."
Told the tale about war and peace
  In the television news.

After them came the soldiers
  With rifle and bomb and gun,
Looking for enemies of the state.
  The family had packed and gone.

When they got back to the village
  The neighbours said, to a man,
"That boy will never be one of us,
  Though he does what he blessed
                          well can."

He went round to all the people
  A paper crown on his head.
Here is some bread from my father.
  Take, eat, he said.

Nobody seemed very hungry.
  Nobody seemed to care.
Nobody saw the god in himself
  Quietly standing there.

He finished up in the papers.
  He came to a very bad end.
He was charged with bringing the
          living to life.
  No man was that prisoner's friend.

There's only one kind of punishment
  To fit that kind of a crime.
They rigged a trial and shot him dead.
  They were only just in time.

They lifted the young man by the leg,
  They lifted him by the arm,
They locked him in a cathedral
  In case he came to harm.

They stored him safe as water
  Under seven rocks,
One Sunday morning he burst out
  Like a jack-in-the-box.

Through the town he went walking.
  He showed them the holes in his head.
Now do you want any loaves? he cried.
  "Not today," they said.

CHARLES CAUSLEY

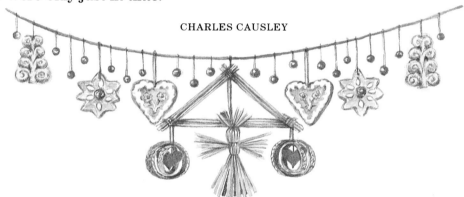

The Children's Carol

Here we come again, again, and here we come again!
Christmas is a single pearl swinging on a chain,
Christmas is a single flower in a barren wood,
Christmas is a single sail on the salty flood,
Christmas is a single star in the empty sky,
Christmas is a single song sung for charity.
Here we come again, again, to sing to you again,
Give a single penny that we may not sing in vain.

ELEANOR FARJEON

Song

Man's a poor deluded bubble,
    Wandering in a mist of lies,
Seeing false, or seeing double,
    Who would trust to such weak eyes?
Yet, presuming on his senses,
    On he goes, most wondrous wise:
Doubts of truth, believes pretences,
    Lost in error lives and dies.

ROBERT DODSLEY

Water

If I were called in
To construct a religion
I should make use of water.

Going to church
Would entail a fording
To dry, different clothes;

The litany would employ
Images of sousing,
A furious devout drench,

And I should raise in the east
A glass of water
Where any-angled light
Would congregate endlessly.

PHILIP LARKIN

Heaven

Fish (fly-replete, in depth of June,
Dawdling away their wat'ry noon)
Ponder deep wisdom, dark or clear,
Each secret fishy hope or fear.
Fish say, they have their Stream and Pond;
But is there anything Beyond?
This life cannot be All, they swear,
For how unpleasant, if it were!
One may not doubt that, somehow, Good
Shall come of Water and of Mud;
And, sure, the reverent eye must see
A Purpose in Liquidity.
We darkly know, by Faith we cry,
The future is not Wholly Dry.
Mud unto mud! – Death eddies near –
Not here the appointed End, not here!
But somewhere, beyond Space and Time,
Is wetter water, slimier slime!
And there (they trust) there swimmeth One
Who swam ere rivers were begun,
Immense, of fishy form and mind,
Squamous, omnipotent, and kind;
And under that Almighty Fin,
The littlest fish may enter in.
Oh! never fly conceals a hook,
Fish say, in the Eternal Brook,
But more than mundane weeds are there,
And mud, celestially fair;
Fat caterpillars drift around,
And Paradisal grubs are found;
Unfading moths, immortal flies,
And the worm that never dies.
And in that Heaven of all their wish,
There shall be no more land, say fish.

RUPERT BROOKE

97

Pippa's Song

The year's at the spring,
And day's at the morn;
Morning's at seven;
The hill-side's dew-pearl'd;
The lark's on the wing;
The snail's on the thorn;
God's in His heaven –
All's right with the world!

ROBERT BROWNING

My Own Epitaph

Life is a jest; and all things show it,
I thought so once; but now I know it.

JOHN GAY

"Here lie I, Martin Elginbrodde"

Here lie I, Martin Elginbrodde:
Ha'e mercy o' my soul, Lord God,
As I wad do, were I Lord God
And ye were Martin Elginbrodde.

ANONYMOUS

Nothing Gold Can Stay

Nature's first green is gold,
Her hardest hue to hold.
Her early leaf's a flower;
But only so an hour.
Then leaf subsides to leaf.
So Eden sank to grief,
So dawn goes down to day.
Nothing gold can stay.

ROBERT FROST

Autumn Fires

In the other gardens
   And all up the vale,
From the autumn bonfires
   See the smoke trail!

Pleasant summer over
   And all the summer flowers,
The red fire blazes,
   The grey smoke towers.

Sing a song of seasons!
   Something bright in all!
Flowers in the summer,
   Fires in the fall!

ROBERT LOUIS STEVENSON

Shroud

Seven threads make the shroud,
The white thread,
A green corn thread,
A blue fish thread,
A red stitch, rut and rieving and wrath,
A gray thread
(All winter failing hand falleth on wheel)
The black thread,
And a thread too bright for the eye.

GEORGE MACKAY BROWN

Hare Drummer

Do the boys and girls still go to Siever's
For cider, after school, in late September?
Or gather hazel nuts among the thickets
On Aaron Hatfield's farm when the frosts begin?
For many times with the laughing girls and boys
Played I along the road and over the hills
When the sun was low and the air was cool,
Stopping to club the walnut tree
Standing leafless against a flaming west.
Now, the smell of the autumn smoke,
And the dropping acorns,
And the echoes about the vales
Bring dreams of life. They hover over me.
They question me:
Where are those laughing comrades?
How many are with me, how many
In the old orchards along the way to Siever's,
And in the woods that overlook
The quiet water?

EDGAR LEE MASTERS

Hare Drummer speaks from the Spoon River cemetery

Laugh and Be Merry

Laugh and be merry, remember, better the world with a
     song,
Better the world with a blow in the teeth of a wrong.
Laugh, for the time is brief, a thread the length of a
     span.
Laugh and be proud to belong to the old proud pageant
     of man.

Laugh and be merry: remember, in olden time,
God made Heaven and Earth for joy He took in a rhyme,
Made them, and filled them full with the strong red wine
     of His mirth,
The splendid joy of the stars: the joy of the earth.

So we must laugh and drink from the deep blue cup of
     the sky,
Join the jubilant song of the great stars sweeping by,
Laugh, and battle, and work, and drink of the wine
     outpoured
In the dear green earth, the sign of the joy of the Lord.

Laugh and be merry together, like brothers akin,
Guesting awhile in the rooms of a beautiful inn,
Glad till the dancing stops, and the lilt of the music ends.
Laugh till the game is played; and be you merry, my
     friends.

JOHN MASEFIELD

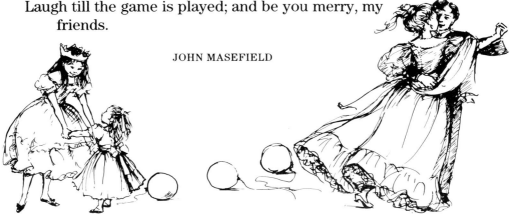

101

The Tide Rises, the Tide Falls

The tide rises, the tide falls,
The twilight darkens, the curlew calls;
Along the sea-sands damp and brown
The traveller hastens toward the town,
　And the tide rises, the tide falls.

Darkness settles on roofs and walls,
But the sea, the sea in the darkness calls;
The little waves, with their soft, white hands,
Efface the footprints in the sands,
　And the tide rises, the tide falls.

The morning breaks; the steeds in their stalls
Stamp and neigh, as the hostler calls;
The day returns, but nevermore
Returns the traveller to the shore,
　And the tide rises, the tide falls.

HENRY WADSWORTH LONGFELLOW

The Animal Kingdom

What Became of Them?

He was a rat, and she was a rat,
   And down in one hole they did dwell;
And both were as black as a witch's cat,
   And they loved one another well.

He had a tail, and she had a tail,
   Both long and curling and fine;
And each said, "Yours is the finest tail
   In the world, excepting mine."

He smelt the cheese, and she smelt the cheese,
   And they both pronounced it good;
And both remarked it would greatly add
   To the charms of their daily food.

So he ventured out, and she ventured out,
   And I saw them go with pain;
But what befell them I never can tell,
   For they never came back again.

ANONYMOUS

"I think I could turn and live with animals"

I think I could turn and live with animals, they are so placid and self-
    contain'd,
I stand and look at them long and long.

They do not sweat and whine about their condition,
They do not lie awake in the dark and weep for their sins,
They do not make me sick discussing their duty to God,
Not one is dissatisfied, not one is demented with the mania of owning
    things,
Not one kneels to another, nor to his kind that lived thousands of years
    ago,
Not one is respectable or unhappy over the whole earth.

So they show their relations to me and I accept them,
They bring me tokens of myself, they evince them plainly in their
    possession.

I wonder where they get those tokens,
Did I pass that way huge times ago and negligently drop them?
Myself moving forward then and now and forever,
Gathering and showing more always and with velocity,
Infinite and omnigenous, and the like of these among them,
Not too exclusive toward the reachers of my remembrancers,
Picking out here one that I love, and now go with him on brotherly
    terms.

A gigantic beauty of a stallion, fresh and responsive to my caresses,
Head high in the forehead, wide between the ears,
Limbs glossy and supple, tail dusting the ground,
Eyes full of sparkling wickedness, ears finely cut, flexibly moving.

His nostrils dilate as my heels embrace him,
His well-built limbs tremble with pleasure as we race around and
     return.
I but use you a minute, then I resign you, stallion,
Why do I need your paces when I myself out-gallop them?
Even as I stand or sit passing faster than you.

WALT WHITMAN

Humming-Bird

I can imagine, in some otherworld
Primeval-dumb, far back
In that most awful stillness, that only gasped and hummed,
Humming-birds raced down the avenues.

Before anything had a soul,
While life was a heave of Matter, half inanimate,
This little bit chipped off in brilliance
And went whizzing through the slow, vast, succulent
     stems.

I believe there were no flowers, then,
In the world where the humming-bird flashed ahead of
     creation.
I believe he pierced the slow vegetable veins with his long
     beak.

Probably he was big
As mosses, and little lizards, they say were once big.
Probably he was a jabbing, terrifying monster.
We look at him through the wrong end of the long
     telescope of Time,
Luckily for us.

D.H. LAWRENCE

Birds

Whatever the bird is, is perfect in the bird.
Weapon kestrel hard as a blade's curve,
thrush round as a mother or a full drop of water
fruit-green parrot wise in his shrieking swerve –
all are what bird is and do not reach beyond bird.

Whatever the bird does is right for the bird to do –
cruel kestrel dividing in his hunger the sky,
thrush in the trembling dew beginning to sing,
parrot clinging and quarrelling and veiling his queer eye –
all these are as birds are and good for birds to do.

But I am torn and beleaguered by my own people.
The blood that feeds my heart is the blood they gave me,
and my heart is the house where they gather and fight –
    for dominion –
all different, all with a wish and a will to save me,
to turn me into the ways of other people.

If I could leave their battleground for the forest of a bird
I could melt the past, the present and the future in one
and find the words that lie behind all these languages.
Then I could fuse my passions into one clear stone
and be simple to myself as the bird is to the bird.

JUDITH WRIGHT

The Boy and the Snake

Henry was every morning fed
With a full mess of milk and bread.
One day the boy his breakfast took,
And ate it by a purling brook
Which through his mother's orchard ran.
From that time ever when he can
Escape his mother's eye, he there
Takes his food in th'open air.
Finding the child delight to eat
Abroad, and make the grass his seat,
His mother lets him have his way.
With free leave Henry every day
Thither repairs, until she heard
Him talking of a fine "grey bird".
This pretty bird, he said, indeed,
Came every day with him to feed,
And it loved him, and loved his milk,
And it was smooth and soft like silk.
His mother thought she'd go and see
What sort of bird this same might be.
So the next morn she follows Harry,
And carefully she sees him carry
Through the long grass his heaped-up mess.
What was her terror and distress,
When she saw the infant take
His bread and milk close to a snake!
Upon the grass he spreads his feast,
And sits down by his frightful guest,
Who had waited for the treat;
And now they both begin to eat.
Fond mother, shriek not! O beware
The least small noise, O have a care –
The least small noise that may be made,
The wily snake will be afraid –
If he hear the lightest sound,
He will inflict th'envenomed wound.

She speaks not, moves not, scarce does breathe,
As she stands the trees beneath;
No sound she utters; and she soon
Sees the child lift up its spoon,
And tap the snake upon the head,
Fearless of harm; and then he said,
As speaking to familiar mate,
"Keep on your own side, do, Grey Pate."
The snake then to the other side,
As one rebuked, seems to glide;
And now again advancing nigh,
Again she hears the infant cry,
Tapping the snake, "Keep further, do;
Mind, Grey Pate, what I say to you."
The danger's o'er! – she sees the boy
(O what a change from fear to joy!)
Rise and bid the snake "goodbye".
Says he, "Our breakfast's done, and I
Will come again tomorrow day",
Then lightly tripping, ran away.

CHARLES AND MARY LAMB

Flying Crooked

The butterfly, a cabbage-white,
(His honest idiocy of flight)
Will never now, it is too late,
Master the art of flying straight,
Yet has – who knows so well as I? –
A just sense of how not to fly:
He lurches here and here by guess
And God and hope and hopelessness.
Even the aerobatic swift
Has not his flying-crooked gift.

ROBERT GRAVES

The Fishes

Oh, a ship she was rigged and ready for sea
And all of her sailors were fishes to be.
Blow the winds westerly, westerly blow,
We're bound to the south'ard, now steady she goes.

Oh first came the herring saying, I'm King of the Sea,
He jumped on the poop, Oh the captain I'll be.

Next came the shark with his two rows of teeth.
Cook, mind you the cabbage and I'll mind the beef.

Then came the porpoise with his little blue snout,
He went to the wheel shouting, Ready about.

Then came the mackerel with his pretty striped back,
He hauled aft each sheet, and he boarded each tack.

Next came the codfish with his chuckle head,
He jumped in the chains and began heaving the lead.

Then came the flounder that lies on the ground,
Saying, Damn your eyes, Chuckle Head, mind how you sound.

Next came the whale, the biggest in the sea,
Shouting, Haul in your head sheets, now hellums a lee.

Last came the sprat, he was smallest of all,
He jumped on the poop crying, Maintops'l haul.

TRADITIONAL

The Tyger

Tyger! Tyger! burning bright
In the forests of the night,
What immortal hand or eye
Could frame thy fearful symmetry?

In what distant deeps or skies
Burnt the fire of thine eyes?
On what wings dare he aspire?
What the hand dare seize the fire?

And what shoulder, and what art,
Could twist the sinews of thy heart?
And when thy heart began to beat,
What dread hand? and what dread feet?

What the hammer? what the chain?
In what furnace was thy brain?
What the anvil? what dread grasp
Dare its deadly terrors clasp?

When the stars threw down their spears,
And water'd heaven with their tears,
Did he smile his work to see?
Did he who made the Lamb make thee?

Tyger! Tyger! burning bright
In the forests of the night,
What immortal hand or eye
Could frame thy fearful symmetry?

WILLIAM BLAKE

111

A Child's Pet

When I sailed out of Baltimore,
    With twice a thousand head of sheep,
They would not eat, they would not drink,
    But bleated o'er the deep.

Inside the pens we crawled each day,
    To sort the living from the dead;
And when we reached the Mersey's mouth,
    Had lost five hundred head.

Yet every night and day one sheep,
    That had no fear of man or sea,
Stuck through the bars its pleading face,
    And it was stroked by me.

And to the sheep-men standing near,
    "You see," I said, "this one tame sheep?
It seems a child has lost her pet,
    And cried herself to sleep."

So every time we passed it by,
    Sailing to England's slaughter-house,
Eight ragged sheep-men – tramps and thieves –
    Would stroke that sheep's black nose.

W.H. DAVIES

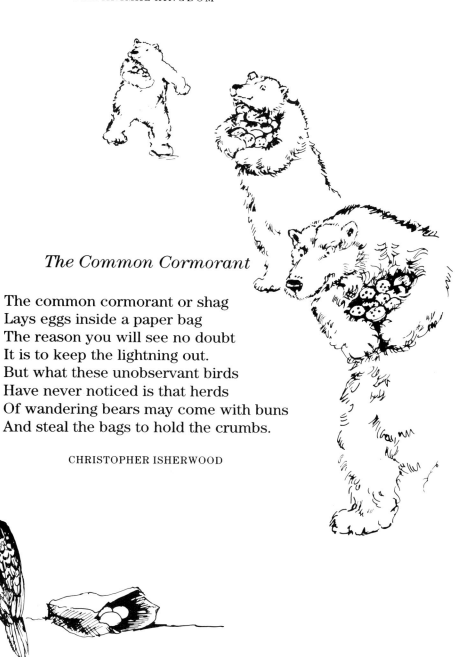

The Common Cormorant

The common cormorant or shag
Lays eggs inside a paper bag
The reason you will see no doubt
It is to keep the lightning out.
But what these unobservant birds
Have never noticed is that herds
Of wandering bears may come with buns
And steal the bags to hold the crumbs.

CHRISTOPHER ISHERWOOD

Cats

Cats sleep
Anywhere,
Any table,
Any chair,
Top of piano,
Window-ledge,
In the middle,
On the edge,
Open drawer,
Empty shoe,
Anybody's
Lap will do,
Fitted in a
Cardboard box,
In the cupboard
With your
frocks –
Anywhere!
They don't care!
Cats sleep
Anywhere.

ELEANOR FARJEON

The Fieldmouse

Where the acorn tumbles down,
   Where the ash tree sheds its berry,
With your fur so soft and brown,
   With your eye so round and merry,
Scarcely moving the long grass,
Fieldmouse, I can see you pass.

Little thing, in what dark den,
   Lie you all the winter sleeping?
Till warm weather comes again,
   Then once more I see you peeping
Round about the tall tree roots,
Nibbling at their fallen fruits.

Fieldmouse, fieldmouse, do not go,
   Where the farmer stacks his treasure,
Find the nut that falls below,
   Eat the acorn at your pleasure,
But you must not steal the grain
He has stacked with so much pain.

Make your hole where mosses spring,
   Underneath the tall oak's shadow,
Pretty, quiet, harmless thing,
   Play about the sunny meadow.
Keep away from corn and house,
None will harm you, little mouse.

CECIL FRANCES ALEXANDER

Macavity: the Mystery Cat

Macavity's a Mystery Cat: he's called the Hidden Paw –
For he's the master criminal who can defy the Law.
He's the bafflement of Scotland Yard, the Flying Squad's despair:
For when they reach the scene of crime – *Macavity's not there!*

Macavity, Macavity, there's no one like Macavity,
He's broken every human law, he breaks the law of gravity.
His powers of levitation would make a fakir stare,
And when you reach the scene of crime – *Macavity's not there!*
You may seek him in the basement, you may look up in the air –
But I tell you once and once again, *Macavity's not there!*

Macavity's a ginger cat, he's very tall and thin;
You would know him if you saw him, for his eyes are sunken in.
His brow is deeply lined with thought, his head is highly domed;
His coat is dusty from neglect, his whiskers are uncombed.
He sways his head from side to side, with movements like a snake;
And when you think he's half asleep, he's always wide awake.

Macavity, Macavity, there's no one like Macavity,
For he's a fiend in feline shape, a monster of depravity.
You may meet him in a by-street, you may see him in the square –
But when a crime's discovered, then *Macavity's not there*!

He's outwardly respectable. (They say he cheats at cards.)
And his footprints are not found in any file of Scotland Yard's.
And when the larder's looted, or the jewel-case is rifled,
Or when the milk is missing, or another Peke's been stifled,
Or the greenhouse glass is broken, and the trellis past repair –
Ay, there's the wonder of the thing! *Macavity's not there*!

And when the Foreign Office find a Treaty's gone astray,
Or the Admiralty lose some plans and drawings by the way,
There may be a scrap of paper in the hall or on the stair –
But it's useless to investigate – *Macavity's not there*!
And when the loss has been disclosed, the Secret Service say:
"It *must* have been Macavity!" – but he's a mile away.
You'll be sure to find him resting, or a-licking of his thumbs,
Or engaged in doing complicated long division sums.

Macavity, Macavity, there's no one like Macavity,
There never was a Cat of such deceitfulness and suavity.
He always has an alibi, and one or two to spare:
At whatever time the deed took place – MACAVITY WASN'T THERE!
And they say that all the Cats whose wicked deeds are widely known
(I might mention Mungojerrie, I might mention Griddlebone)
Are nothing more than agents for the Cat who all the time
Just controls their operations: the Napoleon of Crime!

T.S. ELIOT

117

Poor Old Lady

Poor old lady, she swallowed a fly.
I don't know why she swallowed a fly.
Poor old lady, I think she'll die.

Poor old lady, she swallowed a spider.
It squirmed and wriggled and turned inside her.
She swallowed the spider to catch the fly,
I don't know why she swallowed a fly.
Poor old lady, I think she'll die.

Poor old lady, she swallowed a bird.
How absurd! She swallowed a bird.
She swallowed the bird to catch the spider,
She swallowed the spider to catch the fly,
I don't know why she swallowed a fly.
Poor old lady, I think she'll die.

Poor old lady, she swallowed a cat.
Think of that! She swallowed a cat.
She swallowed the cat to catch the bird,
She swallowed the bird to catch the spider,
She swallowed the spider to catch the fly,
I don't know why she swallowed a fly.
Poor old lady, I think she'll die.

Poor old lady, she swallowed a dog.
She went the whole hog when she swallowed the dog.
She swallowed the dog to catch the cat,
She swallowed the cat to catch the bird,
She swallowed the bird to catch the spider,
She swallowed the spider to catch the fly,
I don't know why she swallowed a fly.
Poor old lady, I think she'll die.

Poor old lady, she swallowed a cow.
I don't know how she swallowed the cow.
She swallowed the cow to catch the dog,
She swallowed the dog to catch the cat,
She swallowed the cat to catch the bird,
She swallowed the bird to catch the spider,
She swallowed the spider to catch the fly,
I don't know why she swallowed a fly.
Poor old lady, I think she'll die.

Poor old lady, she swallowed a horse.
She died, of course.

ANONYMOUS

Upon the Snail

She goes but softly, but she goeth sure;
    She stumbles not as stronger creatures do:
Her journey's shorter, so she may endure
    Better than they which do much further go.

She makes no noise, but stilly seizeth on
    The flower or herb appointed for her food,
The which she quietly doth feed upon,
    While others range, and gare, but find no good.

And though she doth but very softly go,
    However 'tis not fast, nor slow, but sure;
And certainly they that do travel so,
    The prize they do aim at they do procure.

JOHN BUNYAN

The Fallow Deer at the Lonely House

One without looks in to-night
   Through the curtain-chink
From the sheet of glistening white;
One without looks in to-night
   As we sit and think
   By the fender-brink.

We do not discern those eyes
   Watching in the snow;
Lit by lamps of rosy dyes
We do not discern those eyes
   Wondering, aglow,
   Fourfooted, tiptoe.

THOMAS HARDY

Dogs

O little friend, your nose is ready; you sniff,
Asking for that expected walk,
(Your nostrils full of the happy rabbit-whiff)
And almost talk.

And so the moment becomes a moving force;
Coats glide down from their pegs in the humble dark;
You scamper the stairs,
Your body informed with the scent and the track and the mark
Of stoats and weasels, moles and badgers and hares.

We are going *Out.* You know the pitch of the word,
Probing the tone of thought as it comes through fog
And reaches by devious means (half-smelt, half-heard)
The four-legged brain of a walk-ecstatic dog.

Out through the garden your head is already low.
You are going your walk, you know,
And your limbs will draw
Joy from the earth through the touch of your padded paw.

Now, sending a look to us behind,
Who follow slowly the track of your lovely play,
You fetch our bodies forward away from mind
Into the light and fun of your useless day.

Thus, for your walk, we took ourselves, and went
ut by the hedge, and tree, to the open ground.
ι ran, in delightful strata of wafted scent,
· the hill without seeing the view;
ν is hinted through primitive smells to you:
ιt ultimate Beauty you track is but rarely found.

Home . . . and further joy will be waiting there:
Supper full of the lovely taste of bone,
You lift up your nose again, and sniff, and stare
For the rapture known
Of the quick wild gorge of food, then the still lie-down;
While your people will talk above you in the light
Of candles, and your dreams will merge and drown
Into the bed-delicious hours of night.

HAROLD MONRO

Magic and Imagination

Kubla Khan

In Xanadu did Kubla Khan
A stately pleasure-dome decree:
Where Alph, the sacred river, ran
Through caverns measureless to man
   Down to a sunless sea.
So twice five miles of fertile ground
With walls and towers were girdled round:
And there were gardens bright with sinuous rills,
Where blossomed many an incense-bearing tree;
And here were forests ancient as the hills,
Enfolding sunny spots of greenery.

But oh! that deep romantic chasm which slanted
Down the green hill athwart a cedarn cover!
A savage place! as holy and enchanted
As e'er beneath a waning moon was haunted
By woman wailing for her demon-lover!
And from this chasm, with ceaseless turmoil seething,
As if this earth in fast thick pants were breathing,
A mighty fountain momently was forced:
Amid whose swift half-intermitted burst

Huge fragments vaulted like rebounding hail,
Or chaffy grain beneath the thresher's flail:
And 'mid these dancing rocks at once and ever
It flung up momently the sacred river.
Five miles meandering with a mazy motion
Through wood and dale and sacred river ran,
Then reached the caverns measureless to man,
And sank in tumult to a lifeless ocean:
And 'mid this tumult Kubla heard from far
Ancestral voices prophesying war!

    The shadow of the dome of pleasure
    Floated midway on the waves;
    Where was heard the mingled measure
    From the fountain and the caves.
It was a miracle of rare device,
A sunny pleasure-dome with caves of ice!

    A damsel with a dulcimer
    In a vision once I saw:
    It was an Abyssinian maid,
    And on her dulcimer she played,
    Singing of Mount Abora.
    Could I revive within me
    Her symphony and song,
    To such a deep delight 'twould win me,
That with music loud and long,
I would build that dome in air,
That sunny dome! those caves of ice!
And all who heard should see them there,
And all should cry, Beware! Beware!
His flashing eyes, his floating hair!
Weave a circle round him thrice,
And close your eyes with holy dread,
For he on honey-dew hath fed,
And drunk the milk of Paradise.

                SAMUEL TAYLOR COLERIDGE

Blow, Bugle, Blow

The splendour falls on castle walls
    And snowy summits old in story:
The long light shakes across the lakes,
    And the wild cataract leaps in glory.
Blow, bugle, blow, set the wild echoes flying,
Blow, bugle; answer, echoes, dying, dying, dying.

O hark, O hear! how thin and clear,
    And thinner, clearer, farther going!
O sweet and far from cliff and scar
    The horns of Elfland faintly blowing!
Blow, let us hear the purple glens replying:
Blow, bugle; answer, echoes, dying, dying, dying.

O love, they die in yon rich sky,
    They faint on hill or field or river:
Our echoes roll from soul to soul,
    And grow for ever and for ever.
Blow, bugle, blow, set the wild echoes flying,
And answer, echoes, answer, dying, dying, dying.

ALFRED, LORD TENNYSON

A Man in the Wilderness

A man in the wilderness asked of me,
How many red strawberries grow'd in the sea?
I answered him again as well as I could,
So many red herrings as swim'd in the wood.

TRADITIONAL

Jabberwocky

'Twas brillig, and the slithy toves
   Did gyre and gimble in the wabe:
All mimsy were the borogoves,
   And the mome raths outgrabe.

"Beware the Jabberwock, my son!
   The jaws that bite, the claws that catch!
Beware the Jubjub bird, and shun
   The frumious Bandersnatch!"

He took his vorpal sword in hand:
   Long time the manxome foe he sought –
So rested he by the Tumtum tree,
   And stood awhile in thought.

And as in uffish thought he stood,
   The Jabberwock, with eyes of flame,
Came whiffling through the tulgey wood,
   And burbled as it came!

One, two! One, two! And through and through
   The vorpal blade went snicker-snack!
He left it dead, and with its head
   He went galumphing back.

"And hast thou slain the Jabberwock?
   Come to my arms, my beamish boy!
O frabjous day! Callooh! Callay!"
   He chortled in his joy.

'Twas brillig, and the slithy toves
   Did gyre and gimble in the wabe:
All mimsy were the borogoves,
   And the mome raths outgrabe.

LEWIS CARROLL

The Bean-Stalk

Ho, Giant! This is I!
I have built me a bean-stalk into your sky!
La, – but it's lovely, up so high!

This is how I came, – I put
Here my knee, there my foot,
Up and up, from shoot to shoot –
And the blessèd bean-stalk thinning
Like the mischief all the time,
Till it took me rocking, spinning,
In a dizzy, sunny circle,
Making angles with the root,
Far and out above the cackle
Of the city I was born in,
Till the little dirty city
In the light so sheer and sunny
Shone as dazzling bright and pretty
As the money that you find
In a dream of finding money –
What a wind! What a morning! –

Till the tiny, shiny city,
When I shot a glance below,
Shaken with a giddy laughter,
Sick and blissfully afraid,
Was a dew-drop on a blade,
And a pair of moments after
Was the whirling guess I made, –
And the wind was like a whip
Cracking past my icy ears,
And my hair stood out behind,
And my eyes were full of tears,
Wide-open and cold,
More tears than they could hold,

130

The wind was blowing so,
And my teeth were in a row,
Dry and grinning,
And I felt my foot slip,
And I scratched the wind and whined,
And I clutched the stalk and jabbered,
With my eyes shut blind, –
What a wind! What a wind!

Your broad sky, Giant,
Is the shelf of a cupboard;
I make bean-stalks, I'm
A builder, like yourself,
But bean-stalks is my trade,
I couldn't make a shelf,
Don't know how they're made,
Now, a bean-stalk is more pliant –
La, what a climb!

EDNA ST VINCENT MILLAY

131

John Barleycorn

There were three men came out of the west,
Their fortune for to try,
And these three men made a solemn vow,
John Barleycorn should die.
The ploughed, they sowed, they harrowed him in,
Throwed clods upon his head,
And these three men made a solemn vow,
John Barleycorn was dead.

Then they let him lie for a very long time
Till the rain from heaven did fall,
Then little Sir John sprung up his head,
And soon amazed them all.
They let him stand till midsummer
Till he looked both pale and wan,
And little Sir John he growed a long beard
And so became a man.

They hired men with the scythes so sharp
To cut him off at the knee,
They rolled him and tied him by the waist
And served him most barbarously.
They hired men with the sharp pitchforks
Who pricked him to the heart,
And the loader he served him worse than that,
For he bound him to the cart.

They wheeled him round and round the field
Till they came unto a barn,
And there they made a solemn mow
Of poor John Barleycorn.
They hired men with the crabtree sticks
To cut him skin from bone,
And the miller he served him worse than that,
For he ground him between two stones.

Here's little Sir John in a nut-brown bowl,
Here's brandy in a glass;
And little Sir John in the nut-brown bowl
Proved the stronger man at last.
And the huntsman he can't hunt the fox,
Nor so loudly blow his horn,
And the tinker he can't mend kettles or pots
Without a little of Barleycorn.

TRADITIONAL

133

Barley

Barley grain is like seeds of gold bullion.
When you turn a heap with a shovel it pours
With the heavy magic of wealth.
Every grain is a sleeping princess –
Her kingdom is still to come.
She sleeps with sealed lips.
Each grain is like a mouth sealed
Or an eye sealed.
In each mouth the whole bible of barley.
In each eye, the whole sun of barley.
From each single grain, given time,
You could feed the earth.

You treat them rough, dump them into the drill,
Churn them up with a winter supply
Of fertiliser, and steer out onto the tilth
Trailing your wake of grains.

When the field's finished, fresh-damp,
Its stillness is no longer stillness.
The coverlet has been drawn tight again
But now over breathing and dreams.
And the water is already bustling to sponge the
    newcomers.
And the soil, the ancient nurse,
Is assembling everything they will need.
And the angel of earth
Is flying through the field, kissing each one awake.
But it is a hard nursery.
Night and day all through winter huddling naked
They have to listen to pitiless lessons
Of the freezing constellations

And the rain. If it were not for the sun
Who visits them daily, briefly,
To pray with them, they would lose hope
And give up. With him
They recite the Lord's prayer
And sing a psalm. And sometimes at night
When the moon haunts their field and stares down
Into their beds
They sing a psalm softly together
To keep up their courage.

Once their first leaf shivers they sing less
And start working. They cannot miss a day.
They have to get the whole thing right.
Employed by the earth, employed by the sky,
Employed by barley, to be barley.
And now they begin to show their family beauty.
They come charging over the field, under the wind, like
    warriors –
"Terrible as an army with banners",
Barbaric, tireless, Amazon battalions.

And that's how they win their kingdom.
Then they put on gold, for their coronation.
Each one barbed, feathered, a lithe weapon,
Puts on the crown of her kingdom.
Then the whole fieldful of queens
Swirls in a dance
With their invisible partner, the wind,
Like a single dancer.

That is how barley inherits the kingdom of barley.

TED HUGHES

The Stolen Child

Where dips the rocky highland
Of Sleuth Wood in the lake,
There lies a leafy island
Where flapping herons wake
The drowsy water-rats;
There we've hid our faery vats,
Full of berries
And of reddest stolen cherries.
Come away, O human child!
To the waters and the wild
With a faery, hand in hand,
For the world's more full of weeping
  than you can understand.

Where the wave of moonlight glosses
The dim grey sands with light,
Far off by furthest Rosses
We foot it all the night,
Weaving olden dances,
Mingling hands and mingling glances
Till the moon has taken flight;
To and fro we leap
And chase the frothy bubbles,
While the world is full of troubles
And is anxious in its sleep.
Come away, O human child!
To the waters and the wild
With a faery, hand in hand,
For the world's more full of weeping
  than you can understand.

Where the wandering water gushes
From the hills above Glen-Car
In pools among the rushes
That scarce could bathe a star,
We seek for slumbering trout
And whispering in their ears
Give them unquiet dreams;
Leaning softly out
From ferns that drop their tears
Over the young streams.
Come away, O human child!
To the waters and the wild
With a faery, hand in hand,
For the world's more full of weeping
    than you can understand.

Away with us he's going,
The solemn-eyed:
He'll hear no more the lowing
Of the calves on the warm hillside
Or the kettle on the hob
Sing peace into his breast,
Or see the brown mice bob
Round and round the oatmeal-chest.
For he comes, the human child,
To the waters and the wild
With a faery, hand in hand,
From a world more full of weeping
    than he can understand.

W.B. YEATS

Old Rogers is Dead

Old Rogers is dead and is laid in his grave,
    Laid in his grave,
    Laid in his grave;
Old Rogers is dead and is laid in his grave,
    He, hi! laid in his grave.

There grew an old apple tree over his head,
    Over his head,
    Over his head;
There grew an old apple tree over his head,
    He, hi! over his head.

The apples grew ripe, and they all fell off,
    They all fell off,
    They all fell off;
The apples grew ripe, and they all fell off,
    He, hi! they all fell off.

There came an old woman a-picking them up,
    Picking them up,
    Picking them up;
There came an old woman a-picking them up,
    He, hi! picking them up.

Old Rogers jumps up and he gives her a knock,
    Gives her a knock,
    Gives her a knock;
Old Rogers jumps up and he gives her a knock,
    He, hi! gives her a knock.

He makes the old woman go hipperty hop,
    Hipperty hop,
    Hipperty hop;
He makes the old woman go hipperty hop,
    He, hi! hipperty hop.

TRADITIONAL

Spellbound

The night is darkening round me,
The wild winds coldly blow;
But a tyrant spell has bound me
And I cannot, cannot go.

The giant trees are bending
Their bare boughs weighed with snow.
And the storm is fast descending,
And yet I cannot go.

Clouds beyond clouds above me,
Wastes beyond wastes below;
But nothing drear can move me;
I will not, cannot go.

EMILY BRONTË

Fairy Story

I went into the wood one day
And there I walked and lost my way

When it was so dark I could not see
A little creature came to me

He said if I would sing a song
The time would not be very long

But first I must let him hold my hand tight
Or else the wood would give me a fright

I sang a song, he let me go
But now I am home again there is nobody I know.

STEVIE SMITH

The River God

I may be smelly and I may be old,
Rough in my pebbles, reedy in my pools,
But where my fish float by I bless their swimming
And I like the people to bathe in me, especially women.
But I can drown the fools
Who bathe too close to the weir, contrary to rules.
And they take a long time drowning
As I throw them up now and then in a spirit of clowning.
Hi yih, yippity-yap, merrily I flow,
Oh I may be an old foul river but I have plenty of go.
Once there was a lady who was too bold
She bathed in me by the tall black cliff where the water runs cold,
So I brought her down here
To be my beautiful dear.
Oh will she stay with me will she stay
This beautiful lady, or will she go away?
She lies in my beautiful deep river bed with many a weed
To hold her, and many a waving reed.
Oh who would guess what a beautiful white face lies there
Waiting for me to smooth and wash away the fear
She looks at me with. Hi yih, do not let her
Go. There is no one on earth who does not forget her
Now. They say I am a foolish old smelly river
But they do not know of my wide original bed
Where the lady waits, with her golden sleepy head.
If she wishes to go I will not forgive her.

STEVIE SMITH

"There is no Frigate like a Book"

There is no Frigate like a Book
To take us Lands away
Nor any Coursers like a Page
Of prancing Poetry –
This Travel may the poorest take
Without offence of Toll –
How frugal is the Chariot
That bears the Human soul.

EMILY DICKINSON

Beware : Do Not Read This Poem

tonite, thriller was
abt an ol woman, so vain she
surrounded herself w/
     many mirrors

it got so bad that finally she
locked herself indoors & her
whole life became the
     mirrors

one day the villagers broke
into her house , but she was too
swift for them . she disappeared
     into a mirror
each tenant who bought the house
after that , lost a loved one to

     the ol woman in the mirror :
     first a little girl
     then a young woman
     then the young woman/s husband

the hunger of this poem is legendary
it has taken in many victims
back off from this poem
it has drawn in yr feet
back off from this poem
it has drawn in yr legs

back off from this poem
it is a greedy mirror
you are into this poem . from
          the waist down
nobody can hear you can they ?
this poem has had you up to here
          belch
this poem aint got no manners
you cant call out frm this poem
relax now & go w/ this poem

move & roll on to this poem
do not resist this poem
this poem has yr eyes
this poem has his head
this poem has his arms
this poem has his fingers
this poem has his fingertips

this poem is the reader & the
reader this poem

statistic : the us bureau of missing persons
          reports that in 1968 over 100,000 people
          disappeared leaving no solid clues
               nor trace   only
a space   in the lives of their friends

ISHMAEL REED

145

Poetry Jump-Up

Tell me if Ah seeing right
Take a look down de street

Words dancin
words dancin
till dey sweat
words like fishes
jumpin out a net
words wild and free
joinin de poetry revelry
words back to back
words belly to belly

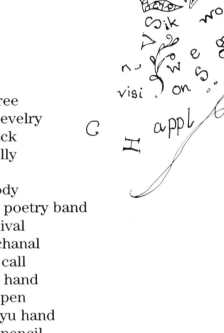

Come on everybody
come and join de poetry band
dis is poetry carnival
dis is poetry bacchanal
when inspiration call
take yu pen in yu hand
if yu dont have a pen
take yu pencil in yu hand
if yu dont have a pencil
what the hell
so long de feeling start to swell
just shout de poem out

Words jumpin off de page
tell me if Ah seeing right
words like birds
jumpin out a cage
take a look down de street
words shakin dey waist
words shakin dey bum
words wit black skin

words wit white skin
words wit brown skin
words wit no skin at all
words huggin up words
an saying I want to be a poem today
rhyme or no rhyme
I is a poem today
I mean to have a good time

Words feeling hot hot hot
big words feeling hot hot hot
lil words feelin hot hot hot
even sad words cant help
tappin dey toe
to de riddum of de poetry band

Dis is poetry carnival
dis is poetry bacchanal
so come on everybody
join de celebration
all yu need is plenty perspiration
an a little inspiration
plenty perspiration
an a little inspiration

JOHN AGARD

Poetry

I, too, dislike it.
    Reading it, however, with a perfect contempt for it, one
        discovers in
    it, after all, a place for the genuine.

MARIANNE MOORE

Lights Out

I have come to the borders of sleep,
The unfathomable deep
Forest, where all must lose
Their way, however straight
Or winding, soon or late;
They can not choose.

Many a road and track
That since the dawn's first crack
Up to the forest brink
Deceived the travellers,
Suddenly now blurs,
And in they sink.

Here love ends –
Despair, ambition ends;
All pleasure and all trouble,
Although most sweet or bitter,
Here ends, in sleep that is sweeter
Than tasks most noble.

There is not any book
Or face of dearest look
That I would not turn from now
To go into the unknown
I must enter, and leave, alone,
I know not how.

The tall forest towers:
Its cloudy foliage lowers
Ahead, shelf above shelf:
Its silence I hear and obey
That I may lose my way
And myself.

EDWARD THOMAS

Nursery Rhyme

For Polly, Whose Eyes Are Tired

Shut your eyes then
And let us slip
Out of the city rain
Into a special ship,
Call her The Pilgrim,
Set sail and go
Over the world's rim
To where Rousseau
Discovered a jungle
Of indigo trees,
A marvelous tangle:
Precise oranges,
Tigers with dreaming eyes,
Larger and larger flowers,
Leaves of gigantic size –
Wander for hours
Under a crimson sun
In a pale milky sky
With a vermilion
Lizard near by,
And over it all
The strangeness that hovers
Like a green pall,
Envelops and covers
In a warm still suspense
All of the landscape

Like a sixth sense –
Till there is no escape,
Till in the grasses
(Two people Rousseau
Saw through his glasses
And wanted to know)
You who have shut your eyes
And I who brought you here
Are to our great surprise
Part of the atmosphere,
Part of the painter's dream,
Of his most intent seeing
In a place where things seem
Instead of being,
No longer living, no longer mortal,
Fabulous ladies,
Unreal, immortal –
Shut then your open eyes
Let us go softly home,
Back to the sleeping ship
Over the emerald foam,
Over the edge and slip
Out of the Rousseau world
Into the world of men,
Sails all bound up and furled:
Open your eyes again.

MAY SARTON

The painter Henri Rousseau is best
known for his childlike paintings of vivid
jungle scenes.

149

O Child, Do Not Fear the Dark and Sleep's Dark Possession

O child, when you go down to sleep and sleep's secession,
You become more and other than you are, you become
       the procession
Of bird and beast and tree: you are a chorus,
A pony among horses, a sapling in a dark forest,
Lifting your limbs and boughs to the sky, leafing.
And then you are one with the beaver, one
With the little animals warm in the sun
Resting and hidden when it is white winter:
       And in sleep's river you sleep
       Like the river's self and the marine
       Beings who mouth as they glide, nosing
         And sliding lithely and smoothly
           Gleaming serenely and sleekly.

DELMORE SCHWARTZ

Index of Poets

Index of Titles and First Lines

Titles are in *italics*. Where the title and first line are the same, the first line only is listed

152

Acknowledgments

We are indebted to the copyright holders for permission to reprint certain poems:

John Agard: to Caroline Sheldon Literary Agency for "Poetry Jump-Up" from BLACK POETRY (Blackie, 1989); Margaret Walker Alexander: to the author for "Lineage" from FOR MY PEOPLE (Yale University Press); Hilaire Belloc: to Peters Fraser & Dunlop Group Ltd. for "The World's End" and "Ha'nacker Mill" from THE COMPLETE VERSE OF HILAIRE BELLOC (Pimlico, a division of Random Century); James Berry: to Hamish Hamilton Ltd and Harcourt Brace Jovanovich Inc. for "One" from WHEN I DANCE (Hamish Hamilton, 1988), copyright © James Berry, 1991; Elizabeth Bishop: to Farrar, Straus & Giroux Inc. for "Manners" from COMPLETE POEMS 1927 – 1979, copyright © 1979, 1983 by Alice Helen Methfessel; Gwendolyn Brooks: to the author for "A song in the front yard" from BLACKS (The David Co., Chicago), copyright © Gwedolyn Brooks, 1987; George Mackay Brown: to John Murray (Publishers) Ltd for "Shroud" from FISHERMEN WITH PLOUGHS (The Hogarth Press, 1971); Charles Causley: to David Higham Associates for "The Ballad of the Breadman" from COLLECTED POEMS, 1951-1975 (Macmillan); John Ciardi: to Judith Ciardi for "The River is a Piece of Sky" from THE SEASON FOR THE PELICAN (J.B. Lippincott Co. 1959); Afua Cooper: to Sister Vision: Black Women and Women of Colour Press, CAFRA and the author for "My Mother" from CREATION FIRE, ed. Ramabai Espinet (1990); Frances Cornford: to Random Century Group on behalf of the Estate of Frances Cornford for "Childhood" from COLLECTED POEMS (Cresset Press, 1954); Countee Cullen: to GRM Associates Inc., Agents for the Estate of Ida M. Cullen for "Incident" from ON THESE I STAND (Harper & Row Publishers). Copyright © 1925 by Harper & Brothers; copyright renewed 1953 by Ida M. Cullen; e.e. cummings: to Liveright Publishing Corporation, Harcourt Brace Jovanovich, Inc. and Harper Collins Publishers for "Maggie and Milly and Molly and May" from SELECTED POEMS 1923 – 1958; Emily Dickinson: to the publishers and the Trustees of Amherst College for "There is no Frigate like a Book" from THE POEMS OF EMILY DICKINSON, ed. Thomas H. Johnson, Cambridge, Mass.: The Belknap Press of Harvard University Press, copyright 1951, © 1955, 1979, 1983 by the President and Fellows of Harvard College; T.S. Eliot: to Faber & Faber Ltd and Harcourt Brace Jovanovich Inc. for "Landscapes: 1. New Hampshire, II. Virginia" from COLLECTED POEMS 1909 – 1962, copyright © 1936 by Harcourt Brace Jovanovich Inc., © 1964, 1963